Milady's

Theory and Practice of
THERAPEUTIC MASSAGE
WORKBOOK

Mark F. Beck

to be used with
Milady's Theory & Practice of Therapuetic Massage
3rd Edition

MILADY
™
THOMSON LEARNING

Africa • Australia • Canada • Denmark • Japan • Mexico • New Zealand • Philippines
Puerto Rico • Singapore • Spain • United Kingdom • United States

NOTICE TO THE READER

Publisher does not warrant or guarantee any of the products described herein or perform any independent analysis in connection with any of the product information contained herein. Publisher does not assume, and expressly disclaims, any obligation to obtain and include information other than that provided to it by the manufacturer.

The reader is expressly warned to consider and adopt all safety precautions that might be indicated by the activities herein and to avoid all potential hazards. By following the instructions contained herein, the reader willingly assumes all risks in connection with such instructions.

The Publisher makes no representation or warranties of any kind, including but not limited to, the warranties of fitness for particular purpose or merchantability, nor are any such representations implied with respect to the material set forth herein, and the publisher takes no responsibility with respect to such material. The publisher shall not be liable for any special, consequential, or exemplary damages resulting, in whole or part, from the readers' use of, or reliance upon, this material.

CONTENTS

How to Use This Workbook

Milady's Theory and Practice of Therapeutic Massage Workbook has been written to meet the needs, interests, and abilities of students receiving training in therapeutic massage.

This workbook should be used together with *Milady's Theory and Practice of Therapeutic Massage*. This workbook directly follows the information found in the student textbook.

Students are to answer each item in this workbook with a pencil after consulting their textbook for correct information. Items can be corrected and/or rated during class or individual discussions, or on an independent study basis.

Various tests are included to emphasize essential facts found in the textbook and to measure the student's progress. "Word Reviews" are listed for each chapter. They are to be used as study guides or for class discussions, or the teacher may assign groups of words for students to use in creative essays.

Exam Review

The exam review at the end of the workbook section serves as an excellent guide for the student preparing for licensing or certification as well as for the experienced massage practitioner. It provides a reliable standard against which professionals can measure their knowledge, understanding, and abilities.

The multiple-choice format has been widely adopted and approved by the majority of state licensing boards. Questions have been grouped by chapter to facilitate review of subject matter after classroom presentations.

The History &
Advancement of
Therapeutic Massage

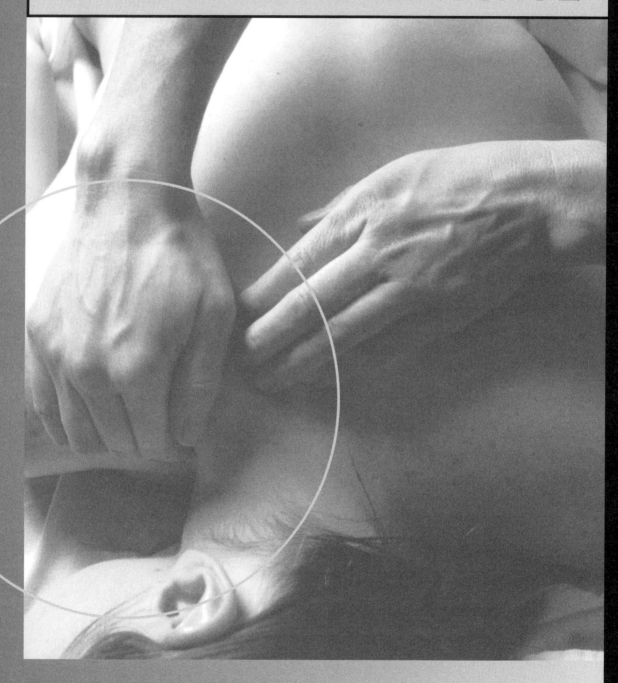

PART I

CHAPTER 1

Historical Overview of Massage

Completion: In the space provided write the word or words that correctly complete each statement.

1. When was the term *massage* first used in American or European literature to denote using the hands to apply manipulations to the soft tissues?

   <u>1875</u> .

2. Two terms the Chinese use for systems of massage are <u>amma</u> and <u>tui-na</u> .

3. There is documentation that the Chinese have practiced massage since <u>3000 BC</u> .

4. The Japanese style of massage that uses finger pressure is <u>shiatsu</u> .

5. A sacred book of the Hindus written around 1800 B.C. is the <u>Ayur-Veda</u> .

6. The Hindu practice of bathing and massage that included kneading the extremities, tapotement, frictioning, anointing with perfumes, and cracking the joints of the fingers, toes, and the neck was known as <u>Tshanpau</u> .

7. The <u>Hippocratic Oath</u> is a code of ethics for physicians and those about to receive medical degrees that binds them to honor their teachers, do their best to maintain the health of their patients, honor their patients' secrets, and prescribe no harmful treatment or drug.

8. The word Hippocrates used to denote the art of rubbing upward not downward is <u>annatriposis</u>.

Matching: Match the name with the best description. Write the letter of that name in the space provided.

A. Aesculapius
B. Avicenna
C. Celcus
D. Dr. James H. Cyriax
E. Elizabeth Dicke
F. Maria Ebner

G. Dr. Douglas O. Graham
H. Hippocrates
I. Albert J. Hoffa
J. Per Henrik Ling
K. Dr. Johann G. Mezger
L. Ambroise Pare

M. Mathias Roth
N. Charles Fayette Taylor
O. George Henry Taylor
R. Emil Vodder

___G.___ 1. Popularized the use of the word *massage* in America

___K.___ 2. Credited with popularizing the terms *effleurage*, *petrissage*, *tapotement*, and *friction*

___A.___ 3. The Greek physician later worshipped as the "god of medicine" who founded the first gymnasium

___H.___ 4. The Greek physician who became known as the father of medicine

___C.___ 5. The name of the Roman physician who wrote *De Medicina*

___B.___ 6. The Persian philosopher/physician who authored the *Canon of Medicine*

___L.___ 7. The French barber/surgeon who was one of the founders of modem surgery and who described in his publications the positive effects of massage in the healing process

___J.___ 8. Known as "the father of physical therapy"; developed a system of movements he called "medical gymnastics"

___M.___ 9. The English physician who published the first book in English on the Swedish movements

___M.___ 10. Established the first institute in England to teach Swedish movement gymnastics

___N.___ 11. The New York physician who introduced the Swedish movements to the United States in 1858

___O.___ 12. Physician's brother who published the first American textbook on the Swedish movement

___K.___ 13. Acknowledged by many of the authors of his day as "the founder of scientific massage"

___G.___ 14. Considered by some to be "the father of Swedish massage in the United States"

___I.___ 15. The distinguished German physician who published *Technik Der Massage*

___R.___ 16. The Austrian who developed a method of lymph massage

___E.___ 17. Developed Bindegewebsmassage

___F.___ 18. Popularized Bindegewebsmassage in England

___D.___ 19. The English orthopedic physician credited with popularizing deep transverse friction massage

Matching: Match the term with the best description. Write the letter of the appropriate term in the space provided.

A. acupressure   C. Rolfing®   E. sports massage

B. reflexology   D. Shiatsu   F. Swedish massage

_F._   1. Based on the Western concepts of anatomy and physiology, and employs effleurage, petrissage, vibration, friction, and tapotement

_A._   2. Based in the Traditional Oriental Medical principles for assessing and treating the physical and energetic body order to regulate Chi (the life force energy)

_D._   3. A finger pressure method based on the Oriental concept that the body has a series of energy (*tsubo*) points

_E._   4. A method of massage especially designed to prepare an athlete for an upcoming event and to aid in the body's regenerative and restorative capacities following a rigorous workout or competition

_C._   5. Developed out of the technique of structural integration, it aligns the major body segments through manipulation of the fascia or the connective tissue

_B._   6. A method based on the idea that stimulation of particular points on the surface of the body has an effect on other areas or organs of the body

CHAPTER 2

Requirements for the Practice of Therapeutic Massage

Short Answer: In the space provided, write a short answer to the following questions.

1. What is meant by "the scope of practice"?

   defines the rights and activities legally acceptable according to the licenses of a particular occupation or profession.

2. In states that have massage licensing, how is the scope of practice defined?

   described in the legal description and definitions contained in the licensing regulation.

3. In the United States what jurisdiction might oversee regulations for massage?

   may fall under the auspices of the state, the county, the municipality or may not exist at all.

4. What is the major reason for licensing massage therapists?

   to curve unethical practices.

5. What is the role of national or state regulatory boards?

   develop & uparade professional standards.

6. Besides massage licensing laws and ordinances, what other laws must be abided when operating a massage business?

   local business and zoning laws

True or False: If the following statements are true, write *true* in the space provided. If they are false, write *false*.

false
~~true~~   1. If a massage therapist is nationally certified, they can practice anywhere in the United States.

false   2. Reciprocity means that if a massage therapist has a license in one place he or she can practice anywhere.

false
~~true~~   3. In a state that has massage licensing, if a licensed nurse or chiropractor wants to practice massage, they must obtain a massage license.

false   4. The scope of practice for massage is clearly defined by national standards.

Short Answer: Of the following statements, put a check mark in front of the ones that may be grounds for revoking, canceling, or suspending a massage license.

✓   1. Having been convicted of a felony

✓   2. Being guilty of fraudulent or deceptive advertising

✓   3. Being engaged currently or previously in any act of prostitution

✓   4. Practicing under a false or assumed name

~~✗~~   5. Being accused of making sexual advances or attempting sexual acts during the course of a massage

✓   6. Prescribing drugs or medicines (unless you are a licensed physician)

    7. Charging extremely high fees for the services provided

✓   8. Being addicted to narcotics, alcohol, or like substances that interfere with the performance of duties

✓   9. Being guilty of fraud or deceit in obtaining a license

    10. Selling nutritional products or other non-massage related items

✓   11. Being willfully negligent in the practice of massage so as to endanger the health of a client

Completion: In the spaces provided, write the word or words that correctly complete each statement.

1. A ___license___ is issued by a state or municipal regulating agency as a requirement for conducting a business or practicing a trade or profession.

2. A document that is awarded in recognition of an accomplishment or for achieving or maintaining some kind of standard is a ___certification___.

C H A P T E R   3

Professional Ethics for Massage Practitioners

Completion: In the spaces provided, write the word or words from the list below that correctly complete each statement.

~~confidential~~	~~fairness~~	~~a satisfied customer~~
~~courtesy~~	~~honest~~	~~sexual~~
~~ethics~~	~~professional~~	~~tactful~~

1. The standards and philosophy of human conduct or code of morals of an individual, group, or profession is known as _ethics_.

2. One of the best forms of advertising in a personal service business is _a satisfied customer_.

3. A person engaged in an avocation or occupation requiring advanced training to gain knowledge and skills is considered a _professional_.

4. All clients should be treated with _courtesy_ and _fairness_.

5. All communications with clients should be _honest_ and _confidential_.

6. Be respectful of the therapeutic relationship and maintain appropriate _sexual_ boundaries.

7. In order to deal with a client who is overly critical, finds fault, and is hard to please, the therapist must be _tactful_.

Short Answer: In the space provided, write a short answer to the following question.

1. List nine attributes that are helpful for developing good communication between therapist and client.

   a. tact - helps you deal deal with hard to please clients.

   b. Cheerfulness - cheerful attitude will go a long way.

   c. patience - ability to be tolerant under stressful situation.

   d. honesty - answer questions in a factual but tactful manner.

   e. intuition - ability to have insight.

   f. sense of humor - helps you to remain optimistic.

   g. maturity - quality of being reliable, responsible, well adjusted.

   h. self-esteem - projected by your attitudes.

   i. self-motivation - ability to set positive goals.

2. Name three ways to stay current regarding the massage profession.

   a. ~~preparation~~ Continue education

   b. ~~planning~~ massage magazines & journals

   c. ~~performance~~ be involved

HUMAN ANATOMY & PHYSIOLOGY

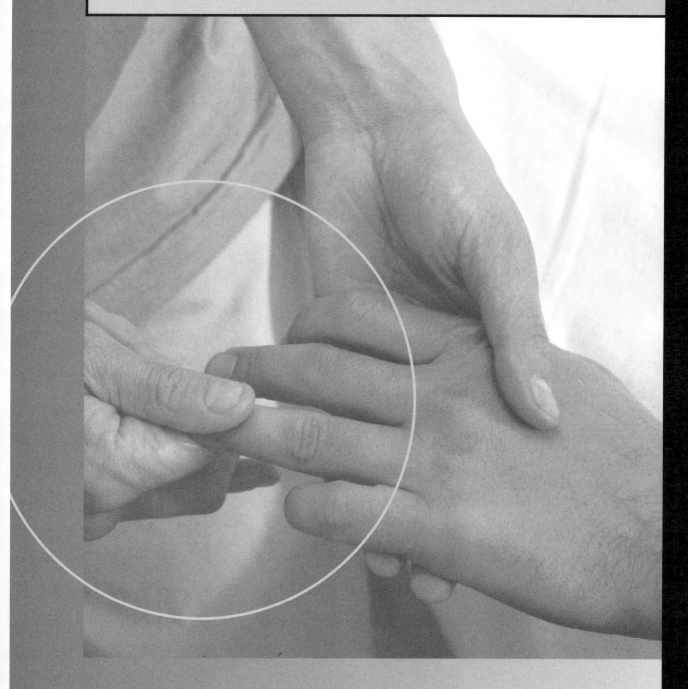

PART II

CHAPTER 4

Overview

Completion: In the space provided, write the word or words that correctly complete each statement.

1. The study of the gross structure of the body or the study of an organism and the interrelations of its parts is _____.

2. The science and study of the vital processes, mechanisms, and functions of an organ or system of organs is _____.

3. The branch of biology concerned with the microscopic structure of tissues of a living organism is _____.

4. The study of the structural and functional changes caused by disease is _____.

5. The scientific study of muscular activity and the mechanics of body movement is _____.

6. The delicate physiological balance the body strives to maintain in its internal environment is _____.

7. The abnormal and unhealthy state of all or part of the body where it is not capable of carrying on its normal function is _____.

8. A _____ of a disease is perceived by the victim while a _____ of a disease is observable by another individual.

Key Choices: Massage may have a direct, an indirect, or a reflex effect on various functions of the body. Put the appropriate letter in the space provided for each of the following phrases.

D = Direct effect

I = Indirect effect

R = Reflex effect

_____ 1. Increased circulation to the muscle and internal organs

_____ 2. Stretching of muscles tissue

_____ 3. Slower, deeper breathing

_____ 4. Loosening of adhesions and scar tissue

_____ 5. Reduced heart rate

_____ 6. Reduced blood pressure

_____ 7. Increased local circulation of venous blood

_____ 8. General relaxation of tense muscles

Key Choices: Most diseases have signs and/or symptoms. Put the appropriate letter in the space provided for each of the following phrases.

X = Disease symptom

O = Sign of disease

_____ 1. nausea

_____ 2. abnormal skin color

_____ 3. pain

_____ 4. chills

_____ 5. elevated pulse

_____ 6. severe itching

_____ 7. abdominal cramps

_____ 8. fever

_____ 9. dizziness

_____ 10. skin ulcers

Completion: In the space provided, write the word or words that correctly completes each statement.

1. Two hormones that are secreted by the adrenal glands are _____ and _____.

2. The protective body sensation that warns of tissue damage or destruction is _____.

3. The two reactions to pain are _____ and _____.

4. Inhibited blood flow to an area of the body is known as _____.

5. A syndrome that often starts as a simple muscle spasm that is complicated by muscle splinting and constricted circulation is the _____.

6. Much of the discomfort in the condition of the previous question is from _____.

7. Psychologically, skillfully applied therapeutic massage helps to reduce pain by relieving _____ and _____.

8. In a pain-spasm-pain cycle, pain is intensified because of _____.

9. Therapeutic massage on contracted ischemic tissue relieves _____ and restores _____.

10. Pain is an indication of _____ or _____.

11. Generally, the more severe the pain the more severe the _____.

12. Bacteria, viruses, fungi, and protozoa are _____.

13. If they enter the body in large enough numbers to multiply and become capable of destroying healthy tissue they cause _____.

14. If these organisms are confined to a small area, the condition is considered a _____, but if they spread through the body, the condition is termed a _____.

15. When tissue is damaged from invading organisms or physical injury, substances are released that cause _____.

16. The four signs and symptoms of inflammation are _____, and _____.

17. An elevated body temperature that accompanies infectious diseases is a _____.

18. The fibrous connective tissue formed as a wound heals is _____. Connective tissue fibers are produced in healing tissue by _____.

Short Answer: In the space provided, write a short answer to the following questions.

1. List six possible direct causes of disease.

   a. _____

   b. _____

   c. _____

   d. _____

   e. _____

   f. _____

2. Stress is most notably associated with the adrenal glands and their secretion of the "fight or flight" hormones. Briefly describe what happens to the following body functions during the "fight or flight" reaction.

   1. Muscle tone _____

   2. Blood pressure _____

   3. Digestion _____

   4. Circulation to skeletal muscles _____

   5. Circulation to digestive organs _____

   6. Red blood cells _____

3. Different types of tissue heal at different rates. Number the following from 1 to 5 according to how fast they mend: 1 is the fastest, 5 is the slowest.

   _____ nerve tissue

   _____ bone

   _____ skin

   _____ muscle

   _____ ligament

Completion: In the space provided, write the word or words that correctly completes each statement.

1. Physiologically, skillfully applied therapeutic massage helps to reduce pain by providing

   _____

   _____.

2. If massage increases the overall intensity of the pain, the therapist should _____

   _____.

3. A wellness-oriented individual attempts to maintain a balance between _____

   _____ and _____.

4. In medical terminology, compound words are constructed of _____

   _____ and _____.

Matching: Match the term in the first column with the meaning in the second column by placing the correct letter in the space provided.

WORD ROOTS I

_____	1. arth(ro)	A.	lung
_____	2. chondr/o	B.	tissue
_____	3. cyt	C.	joint
_____	4. hem	D.	nerve
_____	5. hist	E.	cell
_____	6. my(o)	F.	heat
_____	7. neur(o)	G.	blood
_____	8. oss, ost(e)	H.	vessel
_____	9. phleb	I.	bone
_____	10. pulmo	J.	cartilage
_____	11. therm	K.	vein
_____	12. vas	L.	muscle

WORD ROOTS II

_____	1. brachi	A.	head
_____	2. cardi	B.	kidney
_____	3. cephal	C.	foot
_____	4. derm	D.	stomach
_____	5. gastr(o)	E.	arm
_____	6. gyn	F.	woman
_____	7. hepat	G.	skin
_____	8. labi	H.	lung
_____	9. nephr(o)	I.	liver
_____	10. ocul	J.	heart
_____	11. pneum	K.	eye
_____	12. pod	L.	lip

PREFIXES I

_____	1. ab-	A.	beyond, outside of, in addition
_____	2. ad-	B.	against
_____	3. ant-	C.	against, counter to
_____	4. ante-	D.	away from
_____	5. bio-	E.	inside
_____	6. contra-	F.	above, in addition
_____	7. ex-	G.	before
_____	8. infra-	H.	out of
_____	9. extra-	I.	to, toward
_____	10. intra-	J.	beneath
_____	11. sub-	K.	under, below
_____	12. super-	L.	life

PREFIXES II

_____	1. ect-	A.	under, below
_____	2. end-(o)	B.	one, single
_____	3. epi-	C.	inside, within
_____	4. hyper-	D.	around
_____	5. hypo-	E.	stupor, numbness
_____	6. mega-	F.	upon, over, in addition
_____	7. micr-(o)	G.	large, extreme
_____	8. mon-(o)	H.	outside, without
_____	9. narc-	I.	pertaining to disease
_____	10. path-	J.	small
_____	11. peri-	K.	false
_____	12. pseud-(o)	L.	above, extreme

PREFIXES III

_____	1. hemi-	A.	many, much
_____	2. hetero-	B.	middle, midline
_____	3. hom-	C.	the other
_____	4. medi-	D.	together, along with
_____	5. multi-	E.	four
_____	6. para-	F.	single, one
_____	7. poly-	G.	common, same
_____	8. quad-	H.	many, multiple
_____	9. retro-	I.	half
_____	10. syn-	J.	three
_____	11. tri-	K.	next to, resembling, beside
_____	12. uni-	L.	backward

SUFFIXES

_____	1. -ase	A.	diseased
_____	2. -algia	B.	study of, science of
_____	3. -ectomy	C.	forming an opening
_____	4. -graph	D.	surgical removal of body part
_____	5. -ia	E.	denoting an enzyme
_____	6. -itis	F.	tumor
_____	7. -ology	G.	write, draw, record
_____	8. -oma	H.	morbid fear of
_____	9. -ostomy	I.	excision, cutting into
_____	10. -otomy	J.	painful condition
_____	11. -pathic	K.	inflammation
_____	12. -phobia	L.	a noun ending of a condition

Word Review: The student is encouraged to write down the meaning of each of the following words. The list can be used as a study guide for this unit.

adrenaline	infection	pathology
anatomy	inflammation	physiology
cortisol	ischemia	sign of disease
disease	ischemic pain	stress
fever	kinesiology	symptom
fight or flight	medical terminology	wellness
histology	microorganisms	
homeostasis	pain-spasm-pain cycle	

CHAPTER 5

Human Anatomy and Physiology

Histology

Completion: In the space provided, write the word or words that correctly completes each statement.

1. The submicroscopic particles that make up all substances are called _____.

2. These are arranged in specific patterns and structures called _____.

3. In the human organism, the basic unit of structure and function is the _____.

4. These are organized into layers or groups called _____.

5. Groups of these form complex structures that perform certain functions. These structures are called _____ and are arranged in _____.

6. All living matter is composed of a colorless, jellylike substance called _____.

7. The cytoplasm contains a network of various membranes called _____ which perform specific functions necessary for cell survival.

8. Cell reproduction is controlled by the _____ and the _____.

9. During the early developmental stages of an organism, the repeated division of the ovum results in many specialized cells that differ from one another in composition and function. This process is _____.

10. In the human organism as a cell matures and is nourished, it grows in size and eventually divides into two smaller daughterlike cells. This form of cell division is called _____.

Short Answer: In the space provided, write a short answer to the following questions.

1. Name four ways in which cells differ from one another.

   a. _____   c. _____

   b. _____   d. _____

2. Name the four principal parts of a cell.

a. _____   c. _____

b. _____   d. _____

Identification: Identify the indicated structures in Figure 5.1. Write the correct letter next to the appropriate name in the space provided.

_____ 1. cell membrane   _____ 8. nucleolus

_____ 2. chromatin   _____ 9. nucleus

_____ 3. smooth endoplasmic reticulum _____ 10. ribosomes

_____ 4. Golgi apparatus   _____ 11. vacuole

_____ 5. lysosome   _____ 12. rough endoplasmic reticulum

_____ 6. pinocytic vesicle   _____ 13. cytoplasm

_____ 7. mitochondria   _____ 14. centrioles

Matching: Match each term with its associated function. Write the letter of the function in the space provided.

A. cell membrane   F. Golgi apparatus   K. nucleolus
B. centrosome   G. lysosome   L. nucleus
C. chromatin   H. microtubules   M. ribosome
D. endoplasmic reticulum I. mitochondria   N. vacuole
E. fibrils   J. nuclear membrane

_____ 1. converts and releases energy for cell operation

_____ 2. contains cellular material and transports materials between the inside and outside of the cell

_____ 3. produce lipids or proteins for cell utilization and transport

_____ 4. supervises all cell activity

_____ 5. synthesizes carbohydrates and holds protein for secretion

_____ 6. involved in the rapid introduction or ejection of substances

_____ 7. divides and moves to opposite poles of the cell during mitosis

_____ 8. controls passage of substances between the nucleus and cytoplasm

_____ 9. composed of RNA and protein molecules that synthesize proteins

_____ 10. fibers of protein and DNA that contain the genes

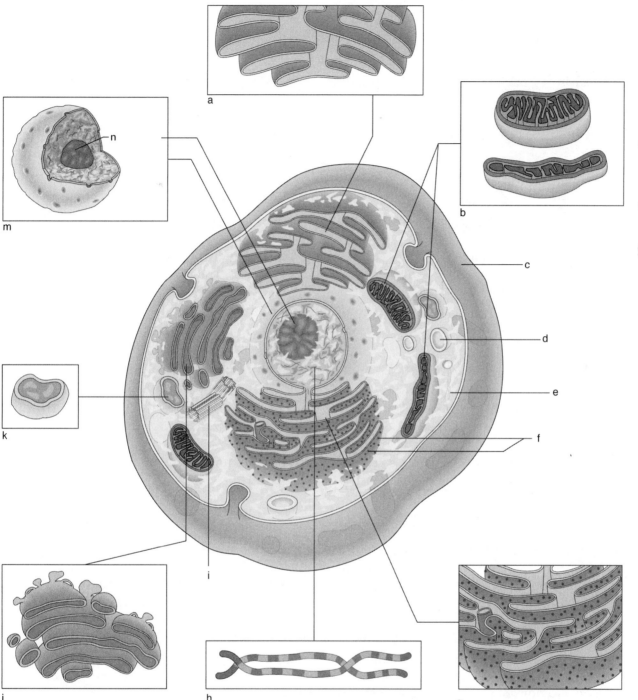

Fig. 5.1   Structure of a typical animal cell

Short Answer: The five phases of cell division are listed below. Number the phases from 1 to 5 to indicate the correct order in which they occur.

_____ metaphase   _____ interphase   _____ anaphase

_____ telophase   _____ prophase

Matching: Match the term with the best description. Write the letter of the best description in the space provided.

_____	1. metaphase	A.	Chromosomes become larger and can be seen as two coiled strands called chromatids.
_____	2. telophase		
_____	3. interphase	B.	This is the normal state of the cell during growth.
_____	4. prophase	C.	Cytoplasm divides into two cells.
_____	5. anaphase	D.	Chromosomes arrange along the equatorial plane.
		E.	The chromatids are separated and are again called chromosomes.

Completion: In the space provided, write the word or words that correctly completes each statement.

1. The chemical reactions within a cell that transform food for cell growth and operation are broadly termed _____.

2. Two phases of metabolism are _____ and _____.

3. The process of building up larger molecules from smaller ones is _____.

4. The process of breaking down larger substances or molecules into smaller ones is _____.

5. Protein substances that act as organic catalysts to initiate, accelerate, or control specific chemical reactions in the metabolic process are called _____.

6. Collections of similar cells that carry out specific functions of the body are called _____.

Short Answer: List the five main categories of tissues in the space provided.

1. _____

2. _____

3. _____

4. _____

5. _____

Identification: In the space provided, write the name of the tissue type that best fits the description.

_____ 1. represented by blood and lymph

_____ 2. functions in the process of absorption, excretion, secretion, and protection

_____ 3. binds structures together and serves as a framework

_____ 4. acts as a channel for the transmission of messages

_____ 5. forms the skin, the covering of the organs, and the inner lining of all the hollow organs

_____ 6. carries nutrients to the cells and carries away waste products

_____ 7. deep fascia, superficial fascia

_____ 8. initiates, controls, and coordinates the body's adaptation to its surroundings

_____ 9. contracts and causes movement

_____ 10. always has a free surface that is exposed to outside influences

_____ 11. responsible for the movement of food through the digestive tract, the constriction of blood vessels, and the emptying of the bladder

_____ 12. bones, cartilage, and ligaments

_____ 13. cells classified by shape as squamous, cuboidal, and columnar

_____ 14. collects into the lymphatic vessels along with metabolic waste and toxins

_____ 15. provides support and protection

_____ 16. covers all the surfaces of the body

_____ 17. responsible for pumping blood through the heart into the blood vessels

_____ 18. composed of neurons

_____ 19. circulates throughout the body

_____ 20. makes up the major tissue of the glands

_____ 21. responsible for facial expression, speaking, and other voluntary movements

Completion: In the space provided, write the word or words that correctly completes each statement.

1. Two categories of membranes are _____ membranes and _____ _____ membranes.

2. _____ produce a thick, sticky substance that acts as a protectant and lubricant.

3. _____ produce a more watery, lubricating substance that lines the body cavities and sometimes forms the outermost surface of the organs contained in those cavities.

4. Three major serous membranes are the _____ that encase the lungs, the _____ around the heart, and the _____ that lines the abdominal cavity.

Short Answer: In the space provided, write a short answer to the question.

1. List three types of fascial membranes.

   a. _____

   b. _____

   c. _____

2. Name three types of skeletal membrane and state where it is found.

   a. _____

   b. _____

   c. _____

Matching: Match the term with the best description. Write the letter of the best description in the space provided.

_____ 1. elastic cartilage	A.	impregnated with mineral salts, chiefly calcium phosphate and calcium carbonate
_____ 2. areolar tissue		
_____ 3. osseous tissue	B.	found between the vertebrae and in the pubic symphysis
_____ 4. adipose tissue		
_____ 5. ligaments	C.	found in the external ear and the larynx
_____ 6. fibrocartilage	D.	found on the end of bones and in movable joints
_____ 7. fibrous connective tissue		
_____ 8. tendons	E.	fibrous bands that connect bones to bones
_____ 9. hyaline cartilage	F.	composed of collagen and elastic fibers that are closely arranged
	G.	cords or bands that serve to attach muscle to bone
	H.	binds the skin to the underlying tissues and fills the spaces between the muscles
	I.	has an abundance of fat-containing cells

Completion: In the space provided, write the word or words that correctly completes each statement.

1. The three types of muscle tissue are _____ and _____.

2. _____ are usually attached to bone or other muscle by way of tendons and can be controlled by conscious effort.

3. Because these muscles have alternating light and dark cross markings, they are called _____.

4. Muscle tissue found in the hollow organs of the stomach, small intestine, colon, bladder, and the blood vessels does not have the cross markings and is called _____ or _____ muscle.

5. _____ is found only in the heart.

Word Review: The student is encouraged to write down the meaning of each of the following words. The list can be used as a study guide for this unit.

adipose tissue	fibrocartilage	perichondrium
amitosis	fibrous connective tissue	periosteum
anabolism	enzymes	physiology
anaphase	epithelial membranes	prophase
anatomy	epithelial tissue	protoplasm
areolar tissue	fascia	reticular tissue
atoms	histology	serous membranes
cardiac muscle tissue	hyaline cartilage	skeletal muscle
catabolism	interphase	smooth muscle
cell	ligaments	squamous
cell membrane	metaphase	striated muscles
cellular metabolism	mitosis	superficial fascia
centrosome	molecules	synovial membrane
columnar	mucous membranes	telophase
connective tissue membranes	nerve tissue	tendons
cuboidal	neurons	tissues
cytoplasm	nucleus	voluntary muscles
cytoplasmic organelles	organ system	
differentiation	organs	

Organization of the Human Body

Completion: In the space provided, write the word or words that correctly completes each statement.

1. In the anatomic position, the body _____ with the palms of the hands facing _____.

2. Anatomists divide the body with three imaginary planes called the _____, the _____, and the _____ planes.

3. The _____ divides the body into left and right parts by an imaginary line running vertically down the body.

4. The _____ is an imaginary line that divides the body into the anterior (front) or ventral half of the body and the posterior (back) or dorsal half of the body.

5. The _____ is an imaginary line that divides the body horizontally into an upper and lower portion.

6. _____ refers to the plane that divides the body or an organ into right and left halves.

Matching: Match the term with the best description. Write the letter of the best description in the space provided.

_____	1. cranial or superior aspect	A.	situated in front of
_____	2. caudal or inferior aspect	B.	situated farther from the crown of the head
_____	3. anterior or ventral aspect	C.	farthest point from the origin of a structure or point of attachment
_____	4. posterior or dorsal aspect		
_____	5. transverse plane	D.	situated in back of
_____	6. sagittal plane	E.	on the side, farther from the midline
_____	7. coronal plane	F.	nearest the origin of a structure or point of attachment
_____	8. medial aspect		
_____	9. lateral aspect	G.	situated toward the crown of the head
_____	10. distal aspect	H.	dividing the body into right and left sides
_____	11. proximal	I.	the frontal plane dividing it into front and back halves
		J.	pertaining to the middle or nearer to the midline
		K.	a plane through a body part perpendicular to the axis

Identification: Figure 5.2 is a diagram of the various body cavities. Identify the indicated structures and write the correct names in the space provided.

1. _____

2. _____

3. _____

4. _____

5. _____

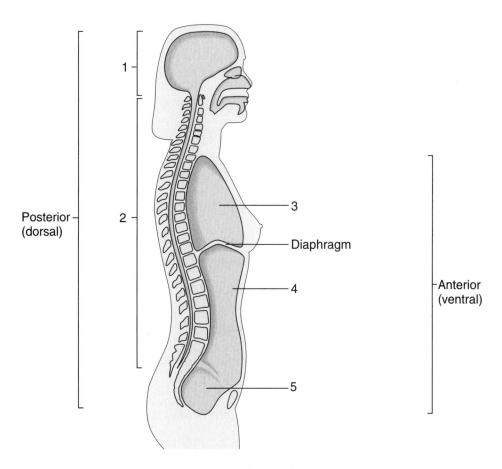

Fig. 5.2   Body cavities

Matching: Match the term with the best description. Write the letter of the best description in the space provided.

_____ 1. hypogastric

_____ 2. inguinal

_____ 3. temporal

_____ 4. scapular

_____ 5. frontal

_____ 6. brachial

_____ 7. cervical

_____ 8. deltoid

_____ 9. umbilical

_____ 10. epigastric

_____ 11. lumbar

_____ 12. gluteal

_____ 13. patellar

_____ 14. popliteal

_____ 15. pectoral

_____ 16. parietal

_____ 17. axillary

_____ 18. femoral

_____ 19. mastoid

_____ 20. hypochondrium

A. region of the temples

B. region of the neck

C. region of the shoulder joint and deltoid muscle

D. region of the armpit

E. region between the elbow and shoulder

F. region of the abdomen lateral to the epigastric region

G. region of the navel

H. region inferior to the umbilical region

I. region of the kneecap

J. region of the thigh

K. region of the groin

L. region of the lower back

M. region of the abdomen

N. region of the breast and chest

O. region of the head, posterior to the frontal region and anterior to the occipital region

P. region of the temporal bone behind the ear

Q. region of muscles of the buttocks

R. region of the back of the shoulder or shoulder blade

S. an area behind the knee joint

T. region of the forehead

Identification: Identify the indicated anatomical areas in Figures 5.3 and 5.4. Write the correct letter next to the appropriate names in the space provided.

_____ 1. axillary

_____ 2. brachial

_____ 3. cervical

_____ 4. epigastric

_____ 5. femoral

_____ 6. frontal

_____ 7. gluteal

_____ 8. hypochondrium

_____ 9. hypogastric

_____ 10. inguinal

_____ 11. lumbar

_____ 12. occipital

_____ 13. parietal

_____ 14. patellar

_____ 15. pectoral

_____ 16. popliteal

_____ 17. sacral

_____ 18. scapular

_____ 19. temporal

_____ 20. umbilical

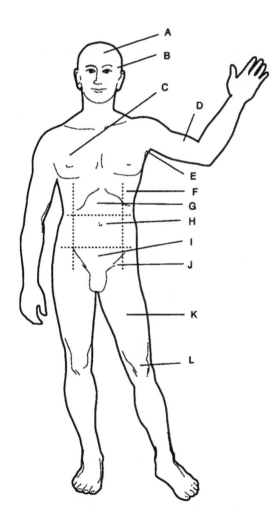

Fig. 5.3 Regions of the body, anterior view

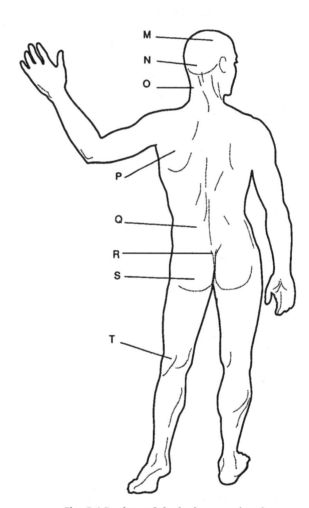

Fig. 5.4 Regions of the body, posterior view

Completion: In the space provided, write the word or words that correctly completes each statement.

1. The dorsal cavities include the _____ cavity and the _____ cavity.

2. The ventral cavities are the _____ cavity and _____ cavities.

3. The liver, stomach, spleen, pancreas, and small and large intestines are located in the _____ cavity.

4. The _____ contains the bladder, rectum, and some of the reproductive organs.

5. The four main anatomical parts of the body are _____, _____, _____ and _____.

6. Body structures containing two or more different tissues that combine to perform a definite function are called _____.

7. When a number of organs work together to perform a bodily function, they comprise an _____.

Short Answer: List ten organ systems.

1. _____

2. _____

3. _____

4. _____

5. _____

6. _____

7. _____

8. _____

9. _____

10. _____

Identification: In the space provided write the name of the related major body system.

_____ 1. carries oxygen and nutrients to all parts of the body

_____ 2. is damaged with a scratch or burn

_____ 3. provides a rigid structure and attachment for muscles

_____ 4. breaks down food into absorbable particles

_____ 5. includes pituitary, thyroid, and ovaries

_____ 6. produces heat and movement

_____ 7. removes uric acid from the system

_____ 8. provides for continuation of the species

_____ 9. allows for the absorption of oxygen into the body

_____ 10. includes the liver, lungs, kidneys, and colon

_____ 11. provides information as to where we are in the environment

_____ 12. produces hormones

Word Review: The student is encouraged to write down the meaning of each of the following words. This list can be used as a study guide for this unit.

abdominal cavities	hormones	proximal
anatomic position	inferior	respiratory system
anterior	integumentary system	sagittal plane
circulatory system	lateral	skeletal system
coronal plane	lymph system	superior
cranial cavity	medial	thoracic cavity
digestive system	muscular system	transverse plane
distal	nervous system	ventral cavities
dorsal cavities	organ system	vertebral cavity
endocrine system	pelvic cavity	
excretory system	posterior	

Short Answer: List six functions of the skin.

1. protection
2. heat regulation
3. secretion & excretion
4. sensation
5. absorption
6. respiration

Identification: Figure 5.5 shows a cross section of skin. Identify the indicated structures and write the correct letter next to the appropriate names in the space provided.

G	1. arrector pili muscle	H	13. sebaceous gland
S	2. dermis	A	14. stratum corneum
T	3. epidermis	E	15. stratum germinativum
I	4. hair root	C	16. stratum granulosum
N	5. adipose	Q	17. subcutaneous tissue
J	6. papilla of hair	V	18. dermal papilla
F	7. capillaries	L	19. sudoriferous gland
M	8. pacinian corpuscle	B	20. stratum lucidum
P	9. vein	D	21. stratum spinosum
X	10. hair shaft	O	22. artery
U	11. Meissner corpuscle	K	23. nerve
R	12. reticular fibers	W	24. sweat pore

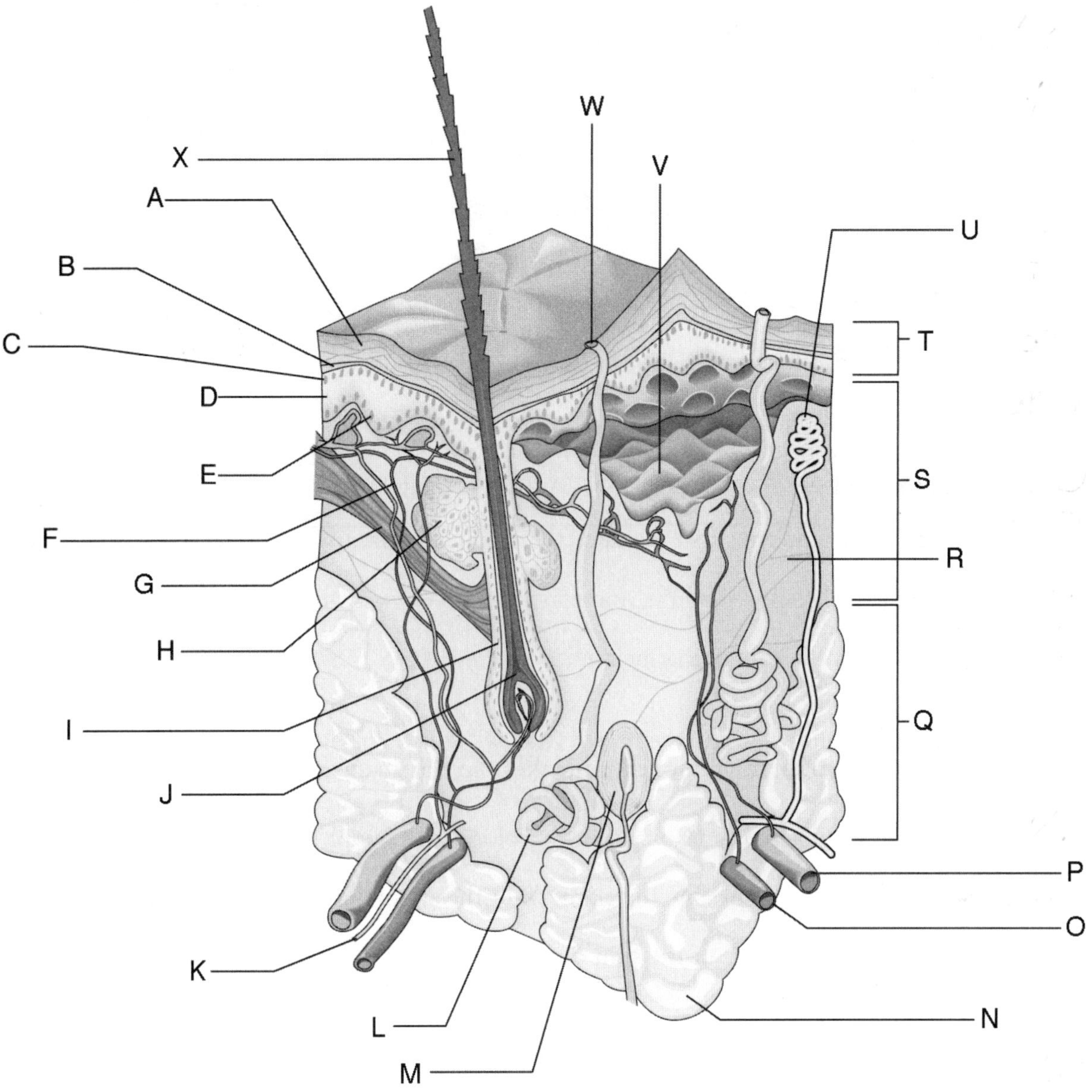

Fig. 5.5   The integumentary system (showing skin and hair)

Matching: Match the term with the best description. Write the letter of that term in the space provided.

A. papillary layer   D. stratum granulosum   G. dermis as a whole
B. reticular layer   E. stratum spinosum   H. epidermis as a whole
C. subcutaneous tissue   F. stratum germinativum

___F___ 1. the deepest layer of the epidermis

___B___ 2. contains fat cells, sweat and oil glands, and hair follicles

___A___ 3. contains conelike projections made of fine strands of elastic tissue extending upward into the epidermis

_H or D_ 4. site of keratin formation

___B___ 5. contains blood and lymph vessels, and nerve endings

___C___ 6. serves as a protective cushion for the upper skin layers

___F___ 7. contains melanocytes that produce the pigment melanin

___G___ 8. contains collagen, reticulum, and elastin fibers

___E___ 9. consists of cells containing melanin

True or False: If the following statements are true, write *true* in the space provided. If they are false, replace the italicized word with one that makes the statement true.

__false__ dermis   1. There is a fine network of blood and lymph capillaries in the *epidermis*.

__true__   2. As people age the *collagen* of the skin tends to lose its elasticity.

__false__ dermis   3. Pliability of the skin depends on elasticity of the fibers in the *subcutaneous layer*.

__true__   4. Healthy skin possesses a slightly *acid* reaction.

__false__ melanin   5. The color of the skin depends on the *thickness* and the blood supply.

Short Answer: Underline the term that does not belong in each of the following groupings.

stratum germinativum	reticular layer	stratum malpighian	stratum granulosum
melanin	collagen	keratin	cuticle
pacinian corpuscle	ruffian receptor	arrector pili	Meissner corpuscle
scar	pustule	crust	fissure
seborrhea	leucoderma	lentigines	naevus

Completion: In the space provided, write the word or words that correctly completes each statement.

1. There are two clearly defined divisions of the skin. The outer layer is the __epidermis__ and the inner layer is the __dermis__.

2. There are two kinds of duct glands in the skin. _sudoriferous_ produce sweat and _sebaceous_ glands produce oil.

3. Sweat glands are under the control of the _autonomic_ nervous system.

4. Two appendages of the skin are _hair_ and _nails_.

5. The appendages of the skin referred to in the previous question are composed of _hard keratin_.

6. The _arrector pili_ muscle is connected to the base of the hair follicle.

7. When the muscle referred to in the previous question contracts, it results in a reaction commonly called _goose bumps_.

8. A structural change in the tissues caused by injury or disease is a _lesion_.

9. A structural change in the tissues that develops in the later stages of disease is called _secondary skin lesion_.

10. Small masses of hardened, discolored sebum that appear most frequently on the face, shoulders, chest, and back are called _black heads_.

Matching: Match the term with the best description. Write the letter of that description in the space provided.

G	1. scar	A.	an accumulation of epidermal flakes such as excessive dandruff
J	2. macule	B.	an itchy, swollen lesion that lasts only a few hours
H	3. pustule	C.	an open lesion on the skin accompanied by loss of skin depth
A	4. scale	D.	a small, elevated pimple in the skin
I	5. tumor	E.	a crack in the skin such as in chapped hands or lips
L	6. vesicle	F.	the scab on a sore
K	7. bulla	G.	likely to form after the healing of an injury
C	8. ulcer	H.	an elevation of the skin having an inflamed base, containing pus
B	9. wheal	I.	an external swelling, varying in size, shape, and color
D	10. papule	J.	a small, discolored spot or patch such as freckles
F	11. crust	K.	a blister similar to but larger than a vesicle
E	12. fissure	L.	a blister with clear fluid in it

37

Completion: In the space provided write the word or words that correctly completes each statement.

1. A skin inflammation caused by outside agents or chemicals is _Contact dermatitis_

2. The most common type of skin cancer is _basal cell carcinoma_

3. The most dangerous type of skin cancer is _malignant melanoma._

4. A mass of connected boils is a _Carbuncle_ .

5. Three types of warts are _common_, _planter_, and _Veneral_ .

6. Three kinds of skin cancer are _basal cell_, _squamos_, and _malig. melanoma cell_

7. The A-B-C-D signs for skin cancer are:

   A - _asymmetry_

   B - _border_

   C - _color_

   D - _diameter_

8. _serisys_ is a chronic, inflammatory skin condition characterized by round dry patches covered with coarse, silvery scales.

9. _impotego_ is a highly contagious, bacterial skin infection that is most common in children.

10. Another name for furuncle is _boil_ .

✳ **Word Review:** The student is encouraged to write down the meaning of each of the following words. The list can be used as a study guide for this unit.

collagen	keratin	stratum granulosum
cuticle	melanin	stratum spinosum
dermis	reticular layer	subcutaneous tissue
epidermis	sebaceous	sudoriferous
integument	stratum germinativum	

38

System Two: The Skeletal System

Short Answer: List the five main functions of the skeletal system.

1. _Support_
2. _Protect_
3. _Movement_
4. _manufacture blood cells_
5. _Store minerals_

Key Choices: Classify each of the following bones in one of four major bone categories by placing the appropriate letter in the space provided.

S = Short bones   I = Irregular bones
L = Long bones   F = Flat bones

__L__ 1. tibia   __I__ 7. axis
__F__ 2. ilium   __L__ 8. femur
__L__ 3. phalange   __S__ 9. talus
__L__ 4. ulna   __L__ 10. metacarpal
__F__ 5. occiput   __F__ 11. scapula
__I__ 6. calcaneus   __F__ 12. rib

Completion: In the space provided, write the word or words that correctly completes each statement.

1. The skeletal system is composed of _bones_ and _cartilage, ligaments._

2. The inorganic mineral matter of bone consists mainly of _calcium phosphate_ and _calcium carbonate._

3. The fibrous membrane covering bone that serves as an attachment for tendons and ligaments is the _periosteum_.

4. The spongy bone tissue in flat bones and at the ends of long bones is filled with _red bone marrow_ and is the site of production for _blood cells_.

5. The hollow chamber formed in the shaft of long bones that is filled with yellow bone marrow is the _medullary cavity_

Identification: Figure 5.6 is a diagram of a typical long bone. Identify the indicated structures and write the correct letters in the space provided.

__G__ 1. proximal epiphysis

__E__ 2. compact bone

__H__ 3. diaphysis (shaft of bone)

__B__ 4. red marrow

__I__ 5. distal epiphysis

__D__ 6. medullary cavity (site of yellow bone marrow in adults)

__F__ 7. periosteum (covering of bone)

__C__ 8. spongy bone

__A__ 9. articular cartilage

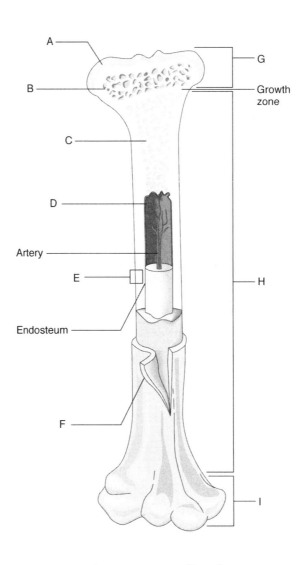

Fig. 5.6 Structure of long bone

Completion: In the space provided, write the word or words that correctly completes each statement.

1. The two main parts of the skeleton are the ___axial___ and the ___appendicular___ _____.

2. The bones of the skull, thorax, vertebral column, and the hyoid bone comprise the ___axial___.

3. The bones of the shoulder, upper extremities, hips, and lower extremities make up the ___appendicular___.

4. In the human adult, the skeleton consists of ___206___ bones.

5. The spine consists of ___24___ vertebra. *26 including sacrum & coccyx*

6. There are ___7___ cervical vertebra.

7. There are ___12___ thoracic vertebra.

8. There are ___5___ lumbar vertebra.

9. There are ___8___ carpals in each wrist.

10. There are ___7___ tarsals in each ankle.

11. There are ___14___ phalanges in each hand.

12. The connection where two bones come together is called a ___joints___ or an ___articulations___.

13. The cranium is composed of ___8___ bones.

14. The face is composed of ___14___ bones.

Key Choices: Joints are classified according to their structure or their function. In the first column of spaces provided, place the appropriate letter indicating the structural classification next to the corresponding terms. In the second column, place the appropriate letter indicating the functional classification next to the corresponding terms.

F = fibrous joints   A = amphiarthrotic joints

C = cartilaginous joints   D = diarthrotic joints

N = synovial joints   S = synarthrotic joints

Functional Classification	Structural Classification		
C	A	1.	symphysis pubis
N	D	2.	glenohumeral joint
F	S	3.	sagittal suture
N	D	4.	elbow joint
F	A	5.	bones united by fibrous connective tissue
N	D	6.	hip joint
F	S	7.	essentially immovable
F	A	8.	sacroiliac joint
N	D	9.	joint capsule with synovial fluid
C	A	10.	intervertebral joints
C	D	11.	articular cartilage on bones
F	S	12.	joint between sphenoid and temporal bones
N	D	13.	freely movable
C	A	14.	allows limited movement

Key Choice: In the space provided, write the letter that corresponds to the appropriate classification of joint. Movable joints in the body are classified as:

A. pivot joints   C. hinge joints   E. saddle joints

B. ball and socket joints   D. gliding joints   F. condylaid joint

_C_ 1. joint between ulna and humerus

_B_ 2. hip joint

_C_ 3. knee joint

_E_ 4. joint between the first metacarpal and the trapezium

_F_ 5. joints between radius and carpals

_B_ 6. glenohumeral joint

_A_ 7. joint between axis and atlas

_A_ 8. joint between radius and ulna near elbow

_D_ 9. intervertebral joints

_C_ 10. interphalangeal joints

_C_ 11. joint between the tibia and the talus

Identification: Identify the bones in Figure 5.7 by writing the correct label in the numbered space that corresponds to the number on the diagram.

1. mandible
2. sternum
3. xiphoid process
4. ulna
5. radius
6. greater trochanter
7. phalanges
8. ischium
9. cranium
10. cervical
11. clavical
12. acromian process
13. coracoid process
14. scapula
15. numerus

16. ribs
17. lumbar
18. illium
19. sacrum
20. coccyx
21. carpals
22. metacarpals
23. femur
24. patella
25. tibia
26. fibula
27. tarsals
28. meta tarsals
29. phalanges

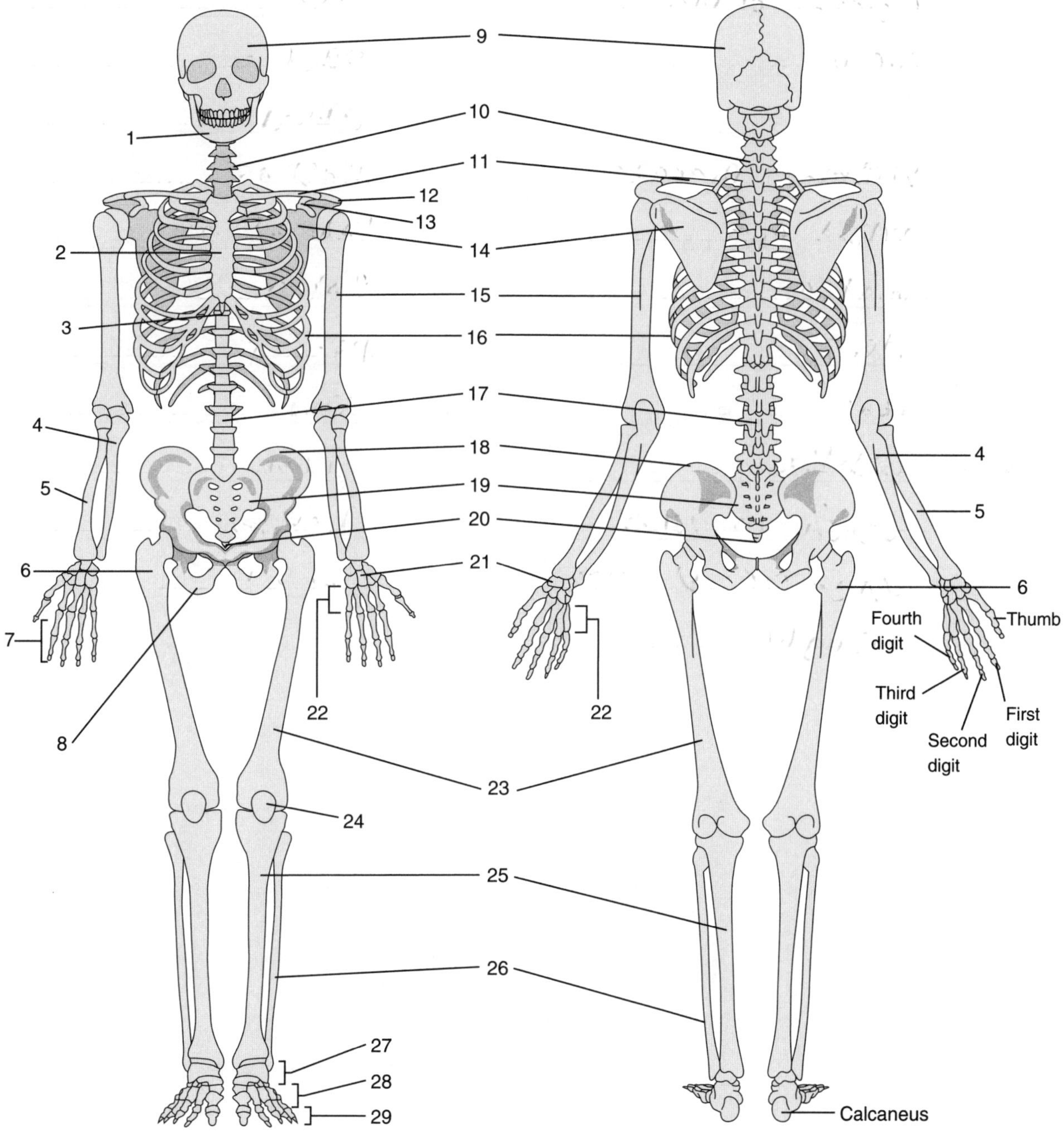

1
2
3
4
5
6
7
8
9
10
11
12
13
14
15
16
17
18
19
20
21
22
22
23
24
25
26
27
28
29

Fourth
digit

Thumb

Third
digit

Second
digit

First
digit

6

Calcaneus

Fig. 5.7   Skeletal system, anterior view

Identification: Identify the bony landmarks in Figures 5.8a and 5.8b by writing the correct name in the lettered space that corresponds to the letter in the diagrams.

A. ramus of mandible

B. sternal notch

C. Coracoid process

D. bicipital groove

_____

E. xiphoid process

F. medial epicondyle of humerus

G. lateral epicondyle of humerus

H. asis

I. pubic arch

J. patella

K. medial malleolus

L. supra-orbital ridge

M. zygomatic arch

N. Acromion process

O. Crest of illium

P. Greater trochanter femur

Q. medial epicondyle femur

R. lateral epicondyle femur

S. head of fibula

T. lateral malleolus

U. calcaneus

V. mastoid process

W. spine of scapula

X. Olecranon process

Y. posterior superior

Z. ischial tuberosity iliac spine

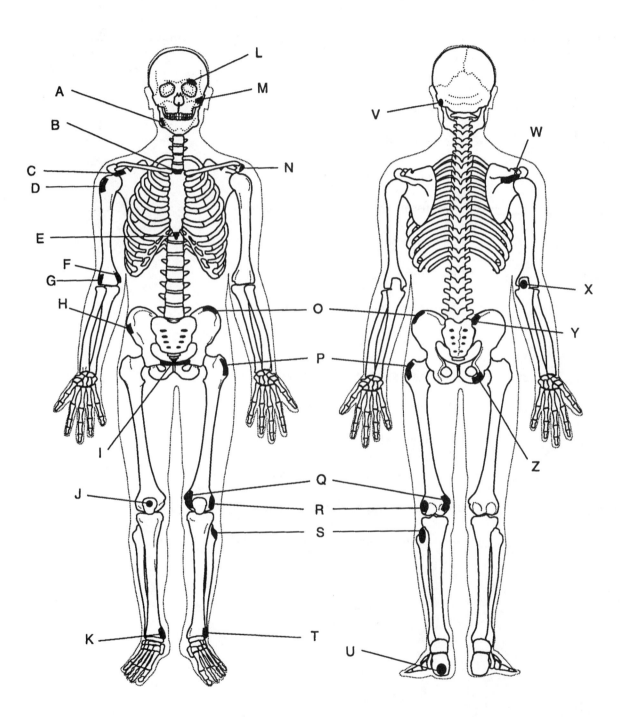

Fig. 5.8a   Major bony landmarks on the body, anterior view

Fig. 5.8b   Major bony landmarks on the body, posterior view

Identification: Identify the bones in Figure 5.9 by writing the correct number next to the appropriate name.

_6_	A. ethmoid	_16_	E. maxilla	_5_	I. sphenoid
_3_	B. frontal	_8_	F. nasal	_4_	J. temporal
_7_	C. lacrimal	_1_	G. occipital	_9_	K. zygomatic arch
_11_	D. mandible	_2_	H. parietal		

Matching: Match the bone names listed above with the best descriptions below. Write the letter of the bone name in the space provided. Note that some descriptions apply to more than one bone.

_K_   1. cheekbone

_E_   2. holds the upper teeth

_____ 3. contains the foramen magnum

_____ 4. forms the supraorbital ridge

_____ 5. four bones containing sinuses

_____ 6. forms the sagittal suture

_____ 7. forms the coronal suture

_____ 8. forms the squamosal suture

_____ 9. forms the lambdoidal suture

_____ 10. forms the mastoid process

_____ 11. forms the chin

_____ 12. connects with all other cranial bones

_____ 13. connected to the skull with a diarthrotic joint

_____ 14. contain openings for tear ducts

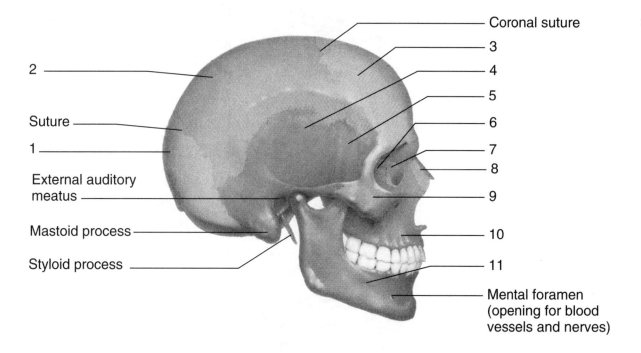

Coronal suture

3

4

5

6

7

8

9

10

11

Mental foramen
(opening for blood
vessels and nerves)

2

Suture

1

External auditory
meatus

Mastoid process

Styloid process

Fig. 5.9   Cranium, neck, and face bones

Identification: Identify the parts of the spine in Figure 5.10 by writing the correct letter next to the corresponding label in the space provided.

_____ atlas, axis   _____ lumbar vertebrae

_____ cervical vertebrae   _____ sacrum

_____ coccyx   _____ thoracic vertebrae

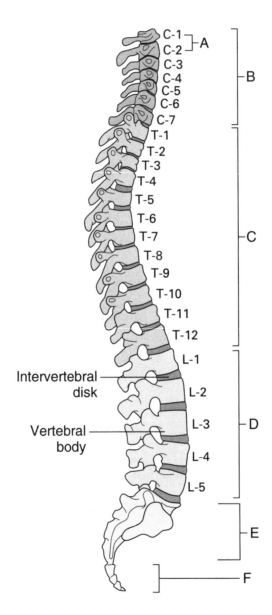

Fig. 5.10 Vertebral column

Matching: Match the term with the best description. Write the letter of the best description in the space provided.

_____ 1. fossa

_____ 2. trochanter

_____ 3. foramen

_____ 4. sinus

_____ 5. process

_____ 6. condyle

_____ 7. line

_____ 8. tuberosity

_____ 9. meatus

_____ 10. tubercle

_____ 11. head

_____ 12. spine

_____ 13. crest

A. a less prominent ridge of a bone than a crest

B. a rounded articulating process at the end of a bone

C. a large process for muscle attachment

D. a sharp slender projection

E. a tubelike passage

F. a depression or hollow

G. a ridge

H. a cavity within a bone

I. a rounded knuckle-like prominence usually at a point of articulation

J. a small rounded process

K. a hole

L. a large rounded process

M. a bone prominence or projection

Short Answer: Circle the term that does not belong in each of the following groupings.

tibia	patella	femur	fibula
elbow	knee	finger	hip
axis/atlas	sacroiliac	intervertebral	pubic symphysis
tubercle	fossa	tuberosity	condyle
cranium	rib	vertebra	scapula

Key Choices: Identify the skeletal disorders by writing the appropriate letter in the space provided.

A. dislocation   C. osteoarthritis   E. fractures   G. bursitis

B. sprain   D. osteoporosis   F. rheumatoid arthritis

_____ 1. an inflammation of the small fluid-filled sacs located near the joints

_____ 2. a break or rupture in a bone

_____ 3. an inflammation causing the articular cartilage to erode and the joints to calcify and eventually become immovable

_____ 4. increased porosity of the bone that causes a thinning of bone tissue

_____ 5. displacement of a bone within a joint

_____ 6. a chronic inflammatory disease, that first affects the synovial membrane lining the joints

_____ 7. stretching or tearing of ligaments

_____ 8. a chronic disease that accompanies aging, usually affecting joints that have experienced a great deal of wear and tear or trauma

Identification: Identify each of the spinal curves in Figure 5.11 by writing the correct label in the space provided.

A. _____   B. _____   C. _____

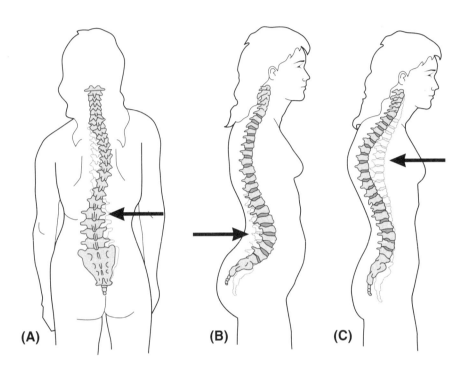

Fig. 5.11   Abnormal curvatures of the spine

Word Review: The student is encouraged to write down the meaning of each of the following words. The list can be used as a study guide for this unit.

amphiarthrotic	cranium	medullary cavity
appendicular skeleton	diaphysis	periosteum
arthritis	diarthrotic	osteoporosis
articular cartilage	epiphysis	scoliosis
articulation	joint capsule	sprain
axial skeleton	kyphosis	synarthrotic
bursa	ligament	synovial fluid
cartilage	lordosis	synovial membrane
compact bone tissue	marrow	vertebra

System Three: The Muscular System

Key Choices: Identify the muscle type described by writing the correct letter(s) in the space provided.

A. skeletal   B. smooth   C. cardiac

_A._ 1. contains striations

_A._ 2. shapes and contours the body

_B._ 3. forms the hollow organs

_B._ 4. involved with transport of materials in the body

_C._ 5. found only in the heart

_B._ 6. spindle shaped

_A._ 7. multinucleated

_B._ 8. controlled by the autonomic nervous system

_C._ 9. quadrangular in shape, joined end to end

_B._ 10. contracts without direct nerve action

_A._ 11. referred to as the muscular system

_C._ 12. coordinates activity to act as a pump

Completion: In the space provided, write the word or words that correctly completes each statement.

1. The main organ of the muscle system is _muscle_ .

2. Muscle cells have the unique ability to _change its length_ .

3. Muscle comprises approximately _40% - 66%_ percent of a person's body weight.

4. The characteristics that enable muscles to perform their functions of contraction and movement are _irritability_ , _contractility_ , and _elasticity_ .

5. The ability to return to its original shape after being stretched is _elasticity_ .

6. The capacity of muscles to receive and react to stimuli is _irritability_ .

7. The ability to contract or shorten and thereby exert force is _contractility_ .

Structure of Skeletal Muscles

Identification: Identify each skeletal muscle part in Figure 5.12 by writing the appropriate number next to the correct term in the space provided.

_____ A. endomysium   _____ E. myofibril   _____ I. sarcoplasm

_____ B. epimysium   _____ F. muscle fiber   _____ J. tendon

_____ C. fascicle   _____ G. perimysium

_____ D. myofilament   _____ H. sarcolemma

Matching: Using the terms listed above, write the letter of the appropriate term in the space provided.

_J._ 1. connective tissue projecting beyond the end of the muscle

_B._ 2. connective tissue covering the entire muscle

_G._ 3. separates muscles into bundles of fibers

_A._ 4. connective tissue covering of each muscle cell

_C._ 5. bundle of muscle fibers

_F._ 6. contractile unit of muscle tissue

_E._ 7. one of the microscopic threads that can be rendered visible in a muscle fiber

_H._ 8. the muscle cell membrane

_D._ 9. structure of the muscle cell containing actin and myosin

_I._ 10. the muscle cell intercellular fluid

Completion: In the space provided, write the word or words that correctly completes each statement.

1. The functional unit of a muscle is the _muscle fiber_ or _muscle cell_ .

2. The cell membrane of the muscle cell is the _sarcolemma_ .

3. The connective tissue covering of the muscle cell is the _endomysium_ .

4. Each muscle cell contains hundreds or even thousands of parallel _myofibrils_ .

5. The interaction of _actin_ and _myosin_ filaments gives muscle its unique contractile ability.

6. The arrangement of _actin_ and _myosin_ gives skeletal muscles a striated or striped appearance.

7. The site where the muscle fiber and nerve fiber meet is called the _neuromuscular junction_ or _myoneural junction_ .

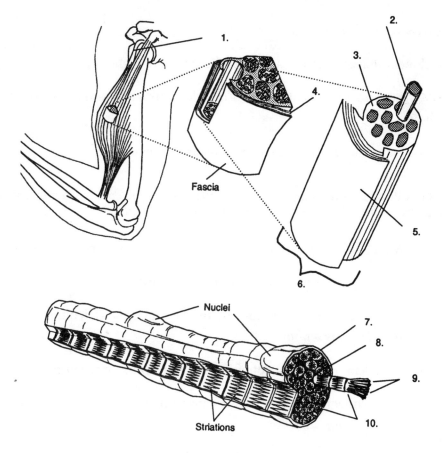

Fascia

Nuclei

1.
2.
3.
4.
5.
6.
7.
8.
9.
10.

Striations

Fig. 5.12 Structure of skeletal muscle

8. A motor neuron and all the muscle fibers that it controls constitute a _motor unit_.

9. When a nerve impulse reaches the end of the nerve fiber, a chemical neurotransmitter called _acetylcholine_ is released.

10. The energy for muscle contraction comes from the breakdown of the _ATP molecule_ _____.

11. A metabolic process known as the _Krebs cycle_ or the _citric acid cycle_ takes place resulting in the synthesis of ATP, and the production of carbon dioxide, water, and energy in the form of heat.

12. When sufficient oxygen is available, ATP is synthesized through _Aerobic cellular_ respiration.

13. When the oxygen supply is depleted, ATP is synthesized through _anaerobic_ respiration.

14. During strenuous activity, heavy breathing and accelerated heart rate are indications of _oxygen debt_.

15. Rapid or prolonged muscle contractions, to the point that oxygen debt becomes extreme and the muscle ceases to respond, causes _muscle fatigue_.

16. A muscle that is firm and responds promptly to stimulation under normal conditions has good _muscle tone_.

17. The most stationary attachment of a muscle is the __Origin__.

18. The muscle attachment that creates the action of the structure is the __insertion__.

19. A(n) __isometric__ contraction occurs when a muscle contracts and the ends of the muscle do not move.

20. The glistening cord that connects the muscle with its attachment is a __tendon__.

True or False: If the following statements are true, write *true* in the space provided. If they are false, replace the italicized word with one that makes the statement true.

__F/ tendons__ 1. Muscle fibers are attached to bone by connective tissue called *ligaments*.

__F/ attach to many__ 2. Each motor nerve attaches to *one* muscle cell.

__True__ 3. The release of calcium ions by the sarcoplasmic reticulum results in a *muscle contraction*.

__True__ 4. A skeletal muscle by definition has *both ends* attached to bone.

__F/ seconds__ 5. Only enough ATP is stored in muscle to sustain a muscle contraction for a few *minutes*.

__True__ 6. ATP is produced by the *mitochondria*.

__True__ 7. An eccentric contraction is an *isotonic* contraction.

Completion: In the space provided, write the word or words that correctly completes each statement.

1. A(n) __eccentric__ contraction occurs when a muscle is contracted and the ends of the muscle move further apart.

2. A(n) __concentric__ contraction occurs when a muscle is contracted and the ends of the muscle move closer together.

3. Eccentric and concentric muscle contractions are both __isotonic__ contractions.

4. When an action occurs, the muscle that is responsible for that action is the __agonist or prime mover__.

5. When an action occurs, the muscle that is responsible for the opposite action is the __antagonist__.

6. Muscles that assist the primary muscle of an action are called __synergist__.

7. When discussing the dynamics of the movement of the body, the three components of motion are __flexion/extension__, __adduction/abduction__, and __rotation__.

Matching: Match the term with the best description. Write the letter of the best description in the space provided.

_____	1. posterior	A.	that which presses or draws down
_____	2. dilator	B.	behind or in back of
_____	3. inferior	C.	pertaining to the middle or center
_____	4. anguli	D.	before or in front of
_____	5. levator	E.	situated lower
_____	6. dorsal	F.	to straighten
_____	7. superior	G.	that which lifts
_____	8. medial	H.	behind or in back of
_____	9. distal	I.	nearer to the center or medial line
_____	10. depressor	J.	at an angle
_____	11. proximal	K.	farther from the center or medial line
_____	12. anterior	L.	situated above
_____	13. extensor	M.	that which expands or enlarges

Matching: Match the term with the best description. Write the letter of the appropriate term in the space provided.

A. flexion	E. adduction	I. medial rotation	M. inversion
B. extension	F. abduction	J. lateral rotation	N. eversion
C. dorsi flexion	G. pronation	K. circumduction	O. elevation
D. plantar flexion	H. supination	L. hyperextension	P. depression

_____ 1. raise the shoulders toward the ears

_____ 2. action of the neck when looking at the ceiling

_____ 3. action of the hip when standing up out of a seated position

_____ 4. action of the toes when standing on tiptoes

_____ 5. turning the hand palm up

_____ 6. action of the foot when pointing toes

_____ 7. action of elbow during eccentric contraction of bicep

_____ 8. bringing the knees together

_____ 9. action of knee during concentric contraction of biceps femoris

_____ 10. turning the sole of the foot medially

_____ 11. action of the femur when turning the feet outward

_____ 12. action of the hip when bringing the knee toward the chest

_____ 13. turning the palm of the hand downward

_____ 14. action of the foot when pointing the toes up toward the knee

Identification: Identify the muscles in Figure 5.13 by writing the correct name in the space provided.

The Muscular System—Anterior View

1. _____

2. _____

3. _____

4. _____

5. _____

6. _____

7. _____

8. _____

9. _____

10. _____

11. _____

12. _____

13. _____

14. _____

15. _____

16. _____

17. _____

18. _____

19. _____

20. _____

21. _____

22. _____

23. _____

24. _____

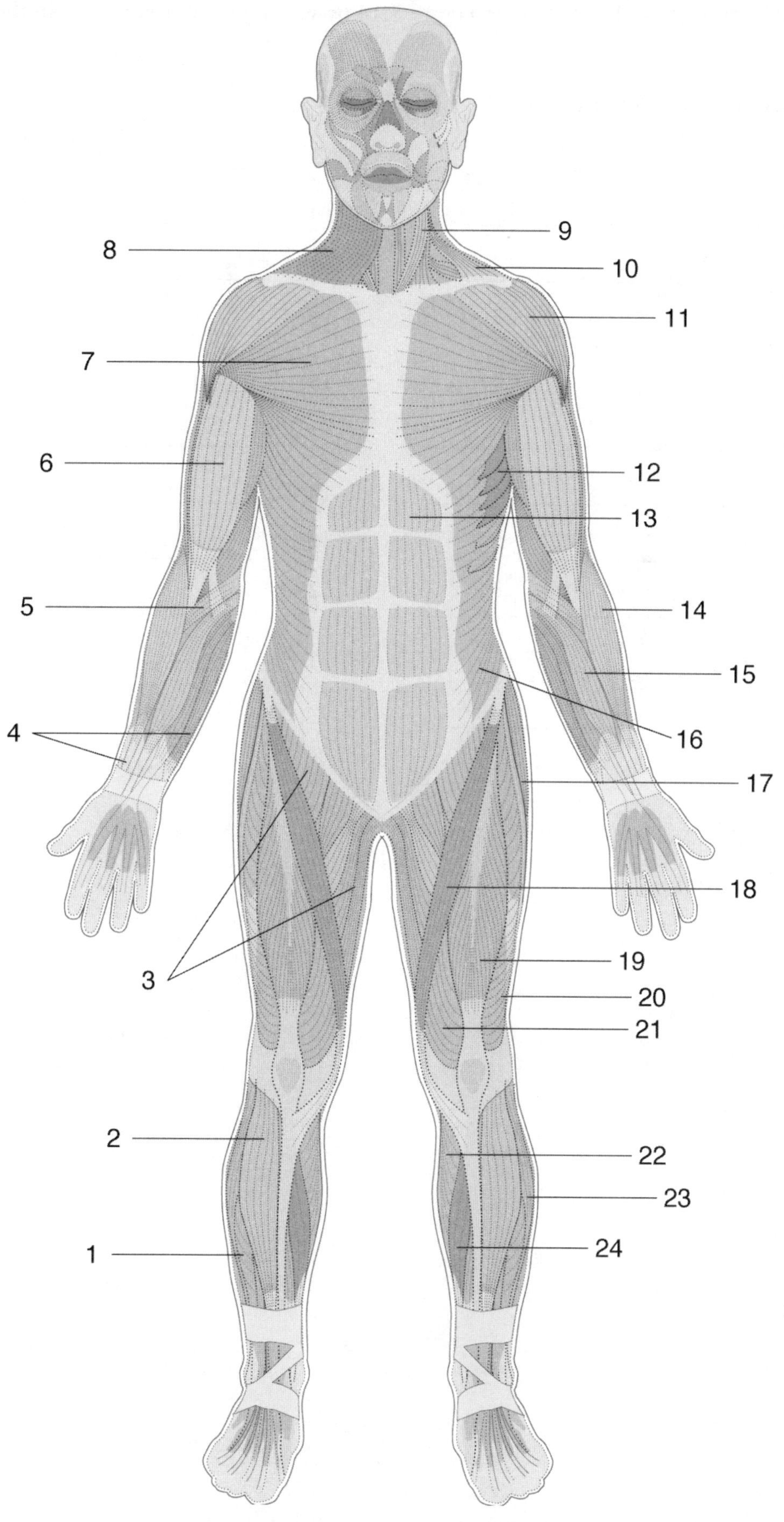

Fig. 5.13   The muscular system, anterior view

Identification: Identify the muscles in Figure 5.14 by writing the correct name in the space provided.

The Muscular System—Posterior View

1. _____

2. _____

3. _____

4. _____

5. _____

6. _____

7. _____

8. _____

9. _____

10. _____

11. _____

12. _____

13. _____

14. _____

15. _____

16. _____

17. _____

18. _____

19. _____

20. _____

21. _____

22. _____

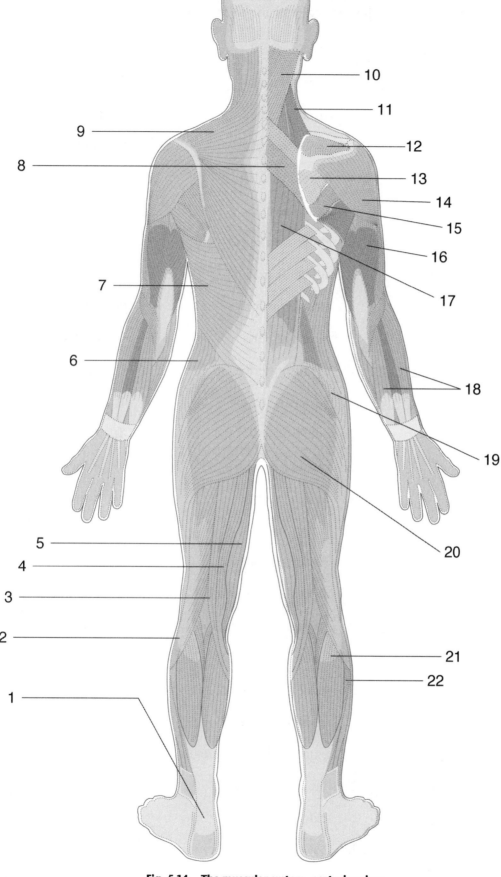

Fig. 5.14   The muscular system, posterior view

Matching: In the first answer column, identify the body part the muscle acts on. Write the correct number in the answer blank. In the second answer column indicate the action the muscle causes when it contracts. Write the correct letter in the answer blank.

Body part   Action

_____   _____   1. gluteus medius   A. Flexes

_____   _____   2. triceps brachii   B. Extends

_____   _____   3. upper trapezius   C. Adducts

_____   _____   4. deltoid (medial)   D. Abducts

_____   _____   5. gastrocnemius   E. Elevates

_____   _____   6. gluteus maximus   F. Plantar flexes

_____   _____   7. adductor magnus   G. Dorsal flexes

_____   _____   8. latissimus dorsi   H. Big toe

_____   _____   9. biceps femoris   I. Elbow

_____   _____   10. tibialis anterior   J. Thumb

_____   _____   11. peroneus longus   K. Hip

_____   _____   12. gracilis   L. Ankle

_____   _____   13. rectus femoris   M. Knee

_____   _____   14. vastus lateralis   N. Scapula

_____   _____   15. biceps brachii   O. Wrist

_____   _____   16. pectoralis major   P. Neck

_____   _____   17. sternocleidomastoid   Q. Shoulder

_____   _____   18. palmaris longus   R. Finger

_____   _____   19. sartorius

_____   _____   20. tensor fascia lata

_____   _____   21. abductor pollicis longus

_____   _____   22. extensor hallucis longus

_____   _____   23. brachioradialis

_____   _____   24. extensor indicus

_____   _____   25. soleus

_____   _____   26. iliopsoas

_____   _____   27. supraspinatus

Completion: In the space provided, write the word or words that correctly completes each statement.

1. A sudden involuntary contraction of a muscle or a group of muscles is a _____.

2. An enlargement of the breadth of a muscle as a result of repeated forceful muscle activity is called _____.

3. When the muscle tissue degenerates and begins to waste away, the process is called _____.

4. The process where muscle tissue is replaced by fibrous connective tissue is _____.

5. Two inflammatory conditions of the white fibrous tissue which cause pain and stiffness (especially the fascial tissues of the muscular system), are _____ and _____.

6. A group of related diseases that seem to be genetically inherited and that cause a progressive degeneration of the voluntary muscular system is _____.

7. _____ is characterized by pain, fatigue, and stiffness in the connective tissue of the muscles, tendons, and ligaments. It is associated with stress and poor sleep habits and is most prevalent in women.

8. An inflammation of the tendon often occurring at the musculotendonis juncture is _____.

9. An inflammation of the tendon sheath that is accompanied by pain and often swelling is called _____.

Short Answer: Circle the term that does not belong in each of the following groups.

brachioradialis	biceps brachii	brachialis	coracobrachialis
biceps femoris	rectus femoris	vastus medialis	vastus lateralis
supraspinatus	subscapularis	teres major	teres minor
pectineus	rectus femoris	adductor longus	gracilis
teres major	pectoralis major	subscapularis	infraspinatus

63

Identification: On the skeleton diagrams in Figures 5.15a through 5.16b, draw by shading the indicated muscles. Be as accurate as possible, paying close attention to muscle attachments. Draw the muscles on the indicated sides to minimize overlap.

Note that the right hand of all of the diagrams are supinated.

Right Hand Side

A. tibialis anterior

B. gracilis

C. adductor longus

D. pectineus

E. tensor fascia latae

F. flexor carpi ulnaris

G. external obliques

H. biceps brachii

I. serratus anterior

Left Hand Side

J. pectoralis minor

K. coracobrachialis

L. rectus abdominis

M. flexor digitorum profundus

N. adductor brevis

O. adductor magnus

P. extensor digitorum longus

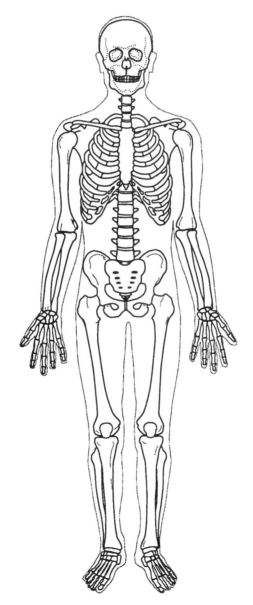

Fig. 5.15a   The skeletal system, anterior view

Right Hand Side

A. peroneus brevis

B. extensor hallucis longus

C. vastus lateralis

D. vastus medialis

E. flexor digitorum superficialis

F. iliacus

G. psoas

H. pectoralis major

I. sternocleidomastoid

Left Hand Side

J. deltoid

K. brachialis

L. quadratus lumborum

M. flexor carpi radialis

N. rectus femoris

O. peroneus longus

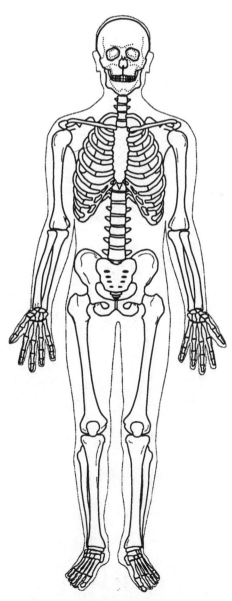

Fig. 5.15b   The skeletal system, anterior view

Left Hand Side

A. flexor digitorum longus

B. biceps femoris

C. semimembranosus

D. gluteus medius

E. brachioradialis

F. latissimus dorsi

G. rhomboids

H. levator scapulae

Right Hand Side

I. trapezius

J. teres major

K. extensor carpi radialis brevis

L. extensor carpi ulnaris

M. gluteus minimus

N. piriformis

O. semitendinosus

P. popliteus

Q. posterior tibialis

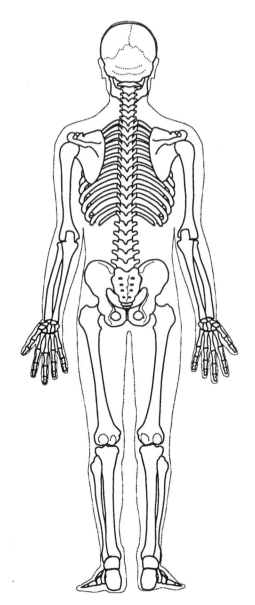

Fig. 5.16a   The skeletal system, posterior view

Left Hand Side

A. gastrocnemius

B. quadratus femoris

C. extensor carpi radialis longus

D. triceps

E. infraspinatus

F. supraspinatus

G. erector spini

Right Hand Side

H. spleneus capitis

I. teres minor

J. extensor digitorum

K. gluteus maximus

L. iliotibial band

M. soleus

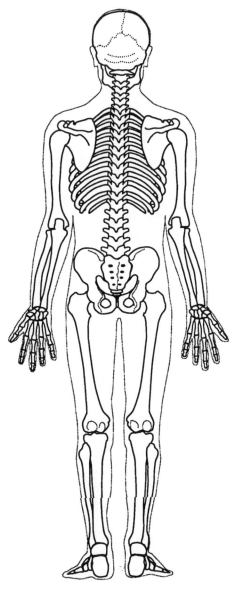

Fig. 5.16b   The skeletal system, posterior view

Word Review: The student is encouraged to write down the meaning of each of the following words. The list can be used as a study guide for this unit.

abduction	fascia	origin
actin	flexion	oxygen debt
adduction	insertion	prime mover
antagonist	motor neuron	pronation
aponeurosis	motor unit	skeletal muscle
cardiac muscle	muscle belly	smooth muscle
contractility	muscle fatigue	striated
elasticity	muscle tone	supination
extensibility	myofibril	synergist
extension	myosin	tendon

System Four: The Circulatory System

Completion: In the space provided, write the word or words that correctly completes each statement.

1. The two divisions to the vascular system are the _Cardiovascular system_ and _lymph-vascular system_.

2. The double-layered membrane that covers the heart is the _pericardium_.

3. The normal heart rate for an adult is _72-80_ beats per minute.

4. The blood vessels that carry blood away from the heart are _Arteries_ and _arterioles_.

5. The blood vessels that carry blood back toward the heart are _veins_ and _venules_.

6. The largest artery in the body is the _aorta_.

7. The smallest, microscopic, thin-walled blood-vessels are called _Capillaries_.

8. The two circulation systems in the blood vascular system are _pulmonary_ and _systemic (general)_.

Identification: Figure 5.17 shows a cross section of a portion of the heart wall including the pericardium. Identify the following parts indicated on the diagram by writing the appropriate letter in the space provided.

____D____ 1. epicardium   ____B.____ 4. parietal pericardium

____C.____ 2. myocardium   ____E.____ 5. pericardial cavity

____A.____ 3. endocardium   ____D.____ 6. visceral pericardium

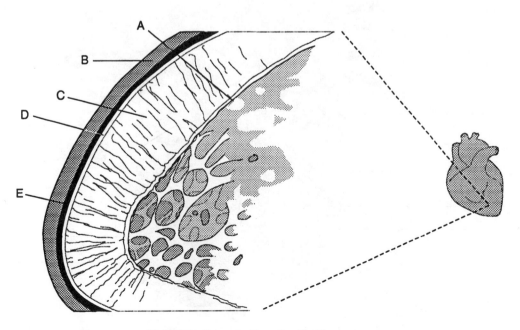

Fig. 5.17   Cross-section of wall of heart

Identification: Figure 5.18 is a diagram of a frontal section of the heart. Identify each indicated structure of the heart by writing the correct letter next to the corresponding term.

_C._ 1. aorta

_I._ 2. aortic semilunar valve

_T._ 3. inferior vena cava

_G._ 4. left atrium

_S._ 5. left ventricle

_H._ 6. mitral (bicuspid) valve

_E._ 7. pulmonary artery

_N._ 8. pulmonary semilunar valve

_F. LM._ 9. pulmonary veins

_O._ 10. right atrium

_R._ 11. right ventricle

_L._ 12. septum

_B._ 13. superior vena cava

_Q._ 14. tricuspid valve

_A._ 15. right pulmonary artery

_S._ 16. endocardium

_P._ 17. percardium

_D._ 18. pulmonary trunk

_K._ 19. myocardium

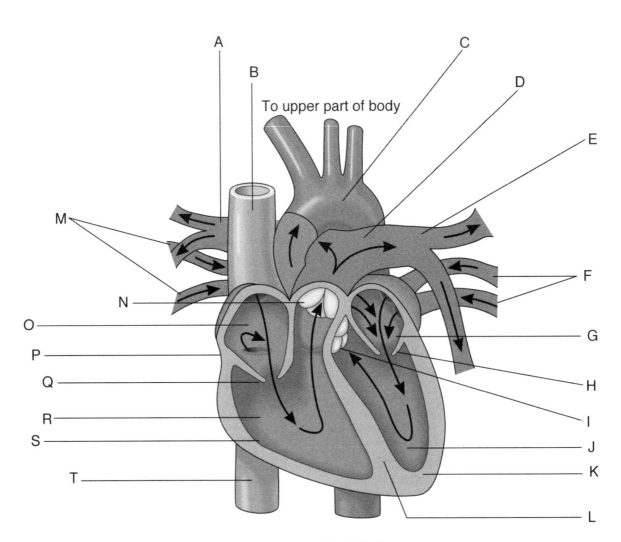

Fig. 5.18 Frontal section of the heart

True or False: If the following statements are true, write *true* in the space provided. If they are false, replace the italicized word with one that makes the statement true.

F. vasoconstriction   1. Impulses from the sympathetic portion of the autonomic nervous system cause *vasodilatation*.

F. diffusion   2. Substances move through the capillary walls mostly by *osmosis*.

True   3. Blood moves through the *arterioles* to the capillaries and then to the *venules*.

F. filtration   4. *Diffusion* is a process where substances move from an area of higher pressure to lower pressure.

True   5. In *pulmonary* circulation, veins contain oxygen-rich blood.

Matching: Match the term with the best description. Write the letter of the appropriate term in the space provided.

A. arteriosclerosis   C. embolus   E. atherosclerosis
B. phlebitis   D. varicose veins   F. edema

D.   1. protruding, bulbous, distended superficial veins

B.   2. an inflammation of a vein

F.   3. a condition of excess fluid in the interstitial spaces

A.   4. the walls of affected arteries tend to thicken, become fibrous, and lose their elasticity

E.   5. an accumulation of fatty deposits on the inner walls of the arteries

C.   6. clots that break loose and float in the blood

True or False: If the following statements are true, write *true* in the space provided. If they are false, replace the italicized word with one that makes the statement true.

F. five   1. The cardio-vascular system of the average adult male contains about *four* liters of blood.

F. alkaline   2. Blood has a slightly *acid* reaction.

F. 55%-60%   3. Plasma accounts for *75* percent of the blood's volume.

F. red   4. *White blood cells* make up as much as 99 percent of all blood cells.

true.   5. Red blood cells and *white blood cells* are produced in the red bone marrow.

Short Answer: Five functions of the blood are listed below. In the space provided, briefly describe how the blood performs these functions.

1. Blood provides nutrients to the cells.

the blood carries water, oxygen, food, and secretions to all areas of the body.

2. Blood removes wastes.

It carries away carbon dioxide and waste products to be eliminated through the excretory channels.

3. Blood maintains normal body temperature.

It helps to equalize the body temp. thus protecting the body from extreme heat & cold.

4. Blood protects against infection.

It aids in protecting the body from harmful microbe and infections through actions of white blood cells.

5. Blood prevents hemorrhaging.

It coagulates (clots).

Completion: In the space provided, write the word or words that correctly completes each statement.

1. The red blood cells are also called _erythrocytes_.

2. Red blood cells are colored with an oxygen-carrying substance called _hemoglobin_.

3. The process where leukocytes actually engulf and digest harmful bacteria is called _phagocytosis_.

4. The small irregularly shaped particles in the blood that play an important role in clotting are _blood platelets_ or _thrombocytes_.

5. A disease characterized by extremely slow clotting of blood and excessive bleeding from even very slight cuts is _hemophilia_.

6. A condition in which there is a rapid loss or inadequate production of red blood cells is _anemia_.

7. A form of cancer in which there is an uncontrolled production of white blood cells is known as _leukemia_.

Identification: Figure 5.19 is a diagram of the major blood vessels of the body. The arteries are indicated on the left side of the body as unshaded vessels. The veins are indicated on the right side of the body as shaded vessels. Identify the numbered blood vessels and write the correct name on the line next to the identifying number.

1. _____
2. _____
3. _left posterior tibial v._
4. _____
5. _____
6. _____
7. _____
8. _____
9. _____
10. _____
11. _____

12. _____
13. _____
14. _____
15. _____
16. _____
17. _____
18. _____
19. _____
20. _____
21. _____

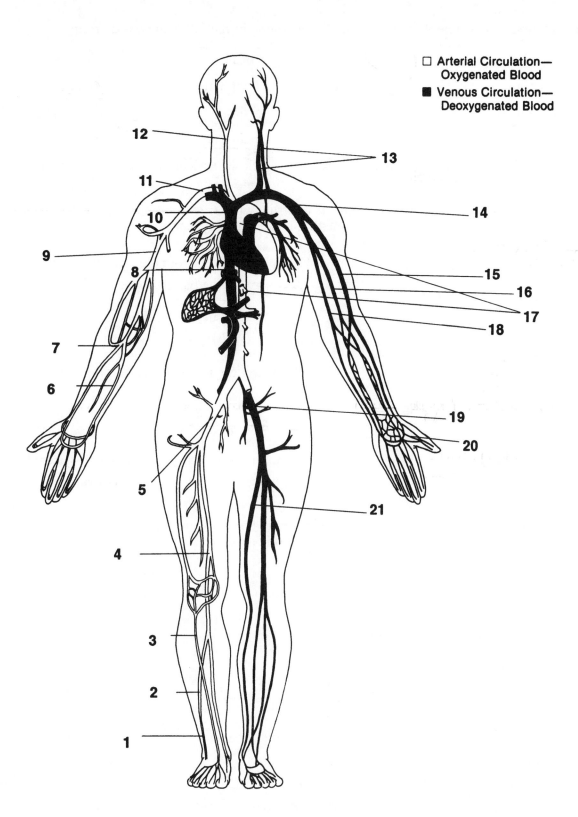

□ Arterial Circulation—
Oxygenated Blood

■ Venous Circulation—
Deoxygenated Blood

Fig. 5.19   Circulatory system

Short Answer: Circle the term that does not belong in the following word groups.

spleen	(liver)	tonsils	thymus
lacteal	thoracic duct	lymphatic	(venule)
swelling	(nausea)	(pain)	redness
lymphocytes	monocytes	(platelets)	leukocytes
(lymph capillaries)	capillary beds	closed system	continuous flow

True or False: If the following statements are true, write *true* in the space provided. If they are false, replace the italicized word with one that makes the statement true.

F. filtered _____

1. Lymph is derived from the interstitial fluid and *produced* by the lymph nodes.

true _____

2. Lymphoid tissue produces a kind of white blood cell called a *lymphocyte*.

true _____

3. *All* lymph eventually flows into the blood stream.

F. right, upper part _____

4. The right lymphatic duct collects lymph from the *right half of the body*.

F. breathing _____

5. Lymph is moved through the lymph system by a pumping action of the *lymph nodes*.

Word Review: The student is encouraged to write down the meaning of each of the following words. The list can be used as a study guide for this unit.

anemia	filtration	plasma
aorta	hemoglobin	platelets
arteriole	interstitial	pulmonary circulation
arteriosclerosis	lacteal	semilunar valves
artery	leukemia	seratonin
atrium	leukocytes	systemic circulation
auricle	lymph	thoracic duct
blood vascular system	lymph vascular system	thrombocytes
capillary	lymphatic pump	tricuspid valve
cardiovascular	lymphatics	vasoconstriction
diffusion	lymphoid tissue	vasodilatation
edema	mitral valve	vasomotor nerves
embolus	myocardium	vein
endocardium	pericardial cavity	vena cava
epicardium	pericardium	ventricle
erythrocytes	phagocytosis	venule
fibrin	phlebitis	

Completion: In the spaces provided write the word or words that correctly completes each statement.

1. Specialized white blood cells called _lymphocytes_ play a major role in the immune response.

2. White blood cells originate in _the red marrow bone marrow._

3. White blood cells specialize into T-cells in the _thymus_.

4. The agent that triggers an immune response is an _antigen_.

5. White blood cells are transported throughout the body by _blood_ and _lymph_.

6. The production of antibodies is the responsibility of the _B-cells_.

7. When the immune system mistakenly attacks itself, the result is _autoimmune_.

8. _T-cells_ attack and destroy antigens directly.

9. The cell that is destroyed by the HIV virus in AIDS is the _CD 4+_.

10. The process of specialized cells engulfing and digesting neutralized antigens and debris is _phagocytosis_.

Matching: Match the terms with the best description. Write the letter of the appropriate term in the answer blank next to the best description.

A. acquired immunity	D. memory cells	G. innate immunity
B. immunity	E. vaccines	H. autoimmune diseases
C. allergen	F. allergy	

_E._ 1. stimulate an immune response without causing the accompanying illness

_B._ 2. all the physiological mechanisms used by the body as protection against foreign substances

_G._ 3. is present from before birth

_C._ 4. allergy-causing substance

_A._ 5. specialized form of immunity that is the result of an encounter with a new substance

_F._ 6. overreaction by your immune system to an otherwise harmless substance

_H._ 7. when the body makes antibodies and T-cells directed against your own cells

_D._ 8. provide immunity for years or even your lifetime

True or False: If the following statement is true, write *true* in the space in front of the statement. If the statement is false, replace the italicized word with one that makes the statement true.

F, HIV 1. *AIDS* disease occurs when the Human Immunodeficiency Virus (HIV) enters a person's body.

_F. 200_ 2. An HIV-infected person is clinically said to have AIDS when their CD4+ T-cell blood count falls below *500* per cubic millimeter of blood.

true 3. HIV is spread most commonly by *sexual contact* with an infected partner or through contact with infected blood.

F. is not 4. Massage *is* contraindicated for people infected with HIV or AIDS.

F. universal 5. Healthcare workers can reduce their risk of becoming HIV infected in their practice by following *safe sex* precautions.

System Five: The Nervous System

Completion: In the space provided, write the word or words that correctly completes each statement.

1. The major parts of the nervous system are the _____ and
   _____.

2. The structural unit of the nervous system is the _____ or _____.

3. There are two types of nerve fibers. _____ connect with other neurons to receive information and a single _____ conducts impulses away from the cell body.

4. Impulses are passed from one neuron to another at a junction called a _____.

5. Two characteristics of a neuron are _____ and _____.

6. Neurons that originate in the periphery and carry information toward the central nervous system (CNS) are _____ or _____ neurons.

7. Neurons that carry impulses from the brain to the muscles or glands that they control are _____ or _____ neurons.

8. Neurons located in the brain and spinal cord that carry impulses from one neuron to another are _____ or _____ neurons.

9. The portion of the nervous system that is surrounded by bone is the
   _____, which consists of the _____ and the _____.

10. The CNS is covered by a special connective tissue membrane called the _____, which has three layers: the _____, the _____, and the _____
    _____.

11. The fluid that surrounds and supports the brain and spinal cord is _____.

12. The largest portion making up the front and top of the brain is the _____.

13. The smaller part of the brain that helps maintain body balance and coordinates voluntary muscles is the _____.

14. The three parts of the brain stem are the _____, the _____, and the _____.

15. The two divisions of the peripheral nervous system are the _____, which involves the nerves to the visceral organs, glands, and blood vessels, and the _____, which involves the nerves to the muscles and skin.

Identification: Figure 5.20 is a diagram of a nerve cell. Identify the indicated structures by writing the letter of the structures next to the correct term.

_____ 1. axon

_____ 2. cell body

_____ 3. dendrites

_____ 4. beads of myelin

_____ 5. nucleus

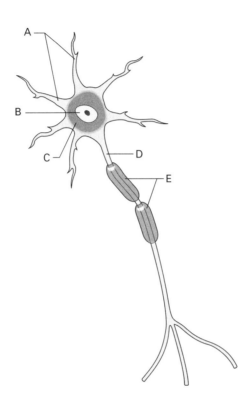

Fig. 5.20   Nerve cell

Matching: Match the term with the best description. Write the letter of the appropriate term in the space provided.

A. afferent neuron

B. axon

C. dendrite

D. efferent neuron

E. ganglion

F. interneuron

G. nerve

H. stimuli

I. synapse

_____ 1. the conducting portion of a neuron

_____ 2. junction point between neurons

_____ 3. bundle of axons in the peripheral nervous system

_____ 4. collection of nerve bodies located outside of the CNS

_____ 5. changes that activate the nervous system

_____ 6. receptive structure of the neuron

_____ 7. carries sensory information toward the CNS

_____ 8. transmits information from one neuron to another

True or False: If the following statements are true, write *true* in the space provided. If they are false, replace the italicized words with one that makes the statement true.

_____ 1. The spinal cord extends from the medulla oblongata to the *sacrum*.

_____ 2. Control centers in the *pons* regulate movements of the heart and control vasoconstriction of the arteries.

_____ 3. The *midbrain* relays impulses from the cerebrum to the cerebellum.

_____ 4. Spinal nerves are numbered according to *the level where they exit the spine*.

_____ 5. There are *thirty-one* pairs of spinal nerves.

_____ 6. All of the nerves outside of the brain and spinal cord are considered to be the *peripheral* nervous system.

Cranial Nerves

Identification and Matching: Number the cranial nerves according to the order in which they arise from the brain. In the first column of answer blanks, write the Roman numeral that corresponds to the cranial nerve. Then, select the best description of the function of the cranial nerve and write the appropriate letter in the second column of answer blanks.

Number   Function

_____ _____ 1. trochlear nerve

_____ _____ 2. optic nerve

_____ _____ 3. hypoglossal nerve

_____ _____ 4. vagus nerve

_____ _____ 5. accessory nerve

_____ _____ 6. abducens nerve

_____ _____ 7. oculomotor nerve

_____ _____ 8. trigeminal nerve

_____ _____ 9. auditory nerve

_____ _____ 10. olfactory nerve

_____ _____ 11. glossopharyngeal nerve

_____ _____ 12. facial nerve

A. speaking, shoulder, and neck muscles

B. sensations of the face and movement of the jaw and tongue

C. moves eyeball down and out

D. sensation and movement related to talking, heart rate, breathing, and digestion

E. sense of smell

F. moves eyeball up, down and in, constricts pupil, raises eyelid

G. tongue movement, and swallowing

H. movements of the face, and salivary glands

I. moves eyeball outward

J. tongue movement, swallowing, sense of taste

K. sense of sight

L. sense of hearing

Short Answer: Write the answers to the following questions in the space provided.

1. How many pairs of cervical nerves are there? _____

2. How many pairs of thoracic nerves are there? _____

3. How many pairs of lumbar nerves are there? _____

4. How many pairs of sacral nerves are there? _____

Identification: Figure 5.21 is a diagram of the major parts of the nervous system. Identify the indicated structures by writing the appropriate letter next to the correct term in the space provided.

_____	1. autonomic chain of ganglia	_____	10. peroneal nerve
_____	2. brachial plexus	_____	11. radial nerve
_____	3. brain	_____	12. sacral plexus
_____	4. cervical plexus	_____	13. saphenous nerve
_____	5. femoral nerve	_____	14. sciatic nerve
_____	6. intercostal nerve	_____	15. spinal cord
_____	7. lumbar plexus	_____	16. tibial nerve
_____	8. median nerve	_____	17. ulnar nerve
_____	9. plantar nerve	_____	18. spinal nerve

A

B

C

D

E

F

G

H

I

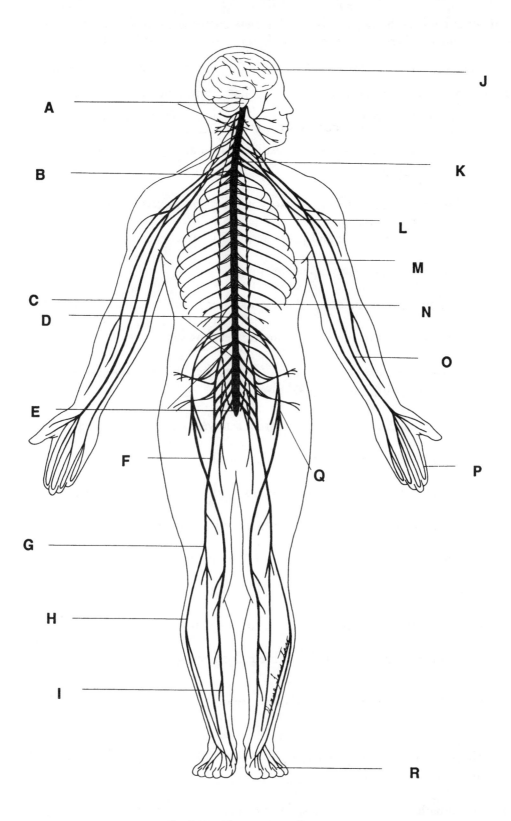

J

K

L

M

N

O

P

Q

R

Fig. 5.21   The nervous system

Key Choices: Choose the key responses that best correspond to the descriptions provided in the following statements. Write the appropriate letter in the space provided.

A. central nervous system
B. peripheral nervous system
C. somatic nervous system
D. autonomic nervous system
E. sympathetic nervous system
F. parasympathetic nervous system

_____ 1. Stimulation causes increased respiration, dilated pupils, increased heart rate, and cardiac output.

_____ 2. Consists of motor nerves, sensory nerves, and mixed nerves.

_____ 3. Is completely housed and protected in a bony covering.

_____ 4. General function is to conserve energy.

_____ 5. Is comprised of the sympathetic and parasympathetic nervous system.

_____ 6. Includes the autonomic and somatic nervous system.

_____ 7. Nerve fibers arise from the vagus nerve, the 2nd, 3rd, and 4th sacral spinal nerves and the III, VII, and IX cranial nerves.

_____ 8. Is composed of cranial nerves, spinal nerves, and nerve ganglia.

_____ 9. Is composed of the brain and spinal cord.

_____ 10. Prepares the organism for energy-expending, stressful, or emergency situations.

_____ 11. Regulates smooth muscle, the heart, and other involuntary functions.

_____ 12. Interprets incoming information and issues orders.

_____ 13. Carries information to and from all parts of the body.

_____ 14. Carries information to and from the skeletal muscles and skin.

_____ 15. Involves a chain of ganglia located along the spine.

Completion: In the space provided, write the word or words that correctly completes each statement.

1. The simplest form of nervous activity that includes a sensory and motor nerve and few, if any, interneurons is called a _____.

2. The nerve pathway of the simplest form of nervous activity is called a _____.

Identification: Figure 5.22 is a diagram of a simple reflex arc. Identify the indicated structures and write the appropriate letter next to the correct term. Note the arrows which indicate the direction of the nerve impulse.

_____ 1. sensory neuron

_____ 2. dorsal root

_____ 3. motor neuron

_____ 4. connecting neuron

_____ 5. sensory nerve receptor

_____ 6. spinal cord

_____ 7. spinal ganglion

_____ 8. ventral root

_____ 9. muscle (effector)

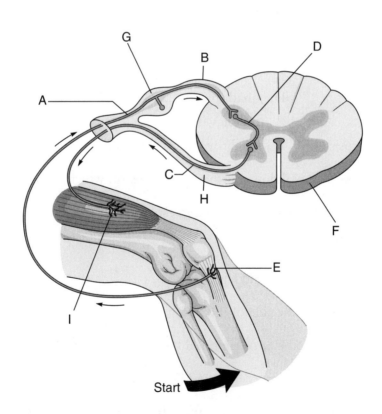

Fig. 5.22 Simple relfex arc

Completion: In the space provided, write the word or words that correctly completes each statement.

1. Sensory nerves that record conscious sensations such as heat, cold, pain, and pressure are termed _____.

2. Sensory nerves that respond to the unconscious inner sense of position and movement of the body are termed _____.

3. The system of sensory and motor nerve activity that provides information as to the position and rate of movement of different body parts is _____.

4. _____ sense the length and stretch of the muscle as well as how far and fast the muscle is moving.

5. _____ consist of intrafusal muscle fibers, annulo-spiral, and flower-type nerve receptors.

6. _____ are multibranched sensory nerve endings located in tendons in the area where muscle fibers attach to tendon tissue.

7. _____ measure the amount of tension produced in muscle cells that occurs as a result of the muscle stretching and contracting.

Matching: Match the term with the best description. Write the letter of the appropriate term in the space provided.

A. paraplegia
B. epilepsy
C. multiple sclerosis
D. quadriplegia
E. poliomyelitis
F. cerebrovascular accident
G. hemiplegia
H. Parkinson's disease

_____ 1. the result of the breakdown of the myelin sheath, which inhibits nerve conduction

_____ 2. characterized by tremors and shaking, especially in the hands

_____ 3. paralysis of lower body

_____ 4. paralysis affecting arms and legs

_____ 5. paralysis affecting one side of the body

_____ 6. the result of a blood clot or ruptured blood vessel in or around the brain

_____ 7. abnormal electrical activity in the CNS characterized by seizures

_____ 8. a crippling or even deadly disease that affects the motor neurons of the medulla oblongata and spinal cord, resulting in paralysis

Word Review: The student is encouraged to write down the meaning of each of the following words. The list can be used as a study guide for this unit.

afferent nerve	ganglia	parasympathetic nervous system
afferent neuron	Golgi tendon organs	peripheral nervous system
arachnoid mater	hemiplegia	pia mater
autonomic nervous system	interneuron	pons
axon	kinesthesia	proprioception
brachial plexus	lumbar plexus	proprioceptors
brain	medulla oblongata	quadriplegia
brain stem	meninges	reflex
central nervous system	midbrain	reflex arc
cerebellum	mixed nerve	sacral plexus
cerebrospinal fluid	motor nerve	sciatic nerve
cerebrovascular accident	motor neuron	sciatica
cerebrum	muscle spindle cells	sensory nerve
cervical plexus	nerve	sensory neuron
cranial nerves	nerve cell	somatic nervous system
dendrite	nerve fibers	spinal cord
dura mater	neuralgia	spinal cord injury
effector	neuritis	stroke
efferent nerve	neuron	sympathetic nervous system
efferent neuron	neurotransmitter	synapse
epilepsy	paraplegia	

Completion: In the space provided, write the word or words that correctly completes each statement.

1. Glands that have tubes or ducts that carry their secretions to a particular part of the body are _____ or _____.

2. Glands that depend on the blood and lymph to carry their secretions to various affected tissues are _____ glands.

3. The chemical substances manufactured by the endocrine glands are known as _____.

Identification: Figure 5.23 is a diagram of the endocrine glands of the body. In the space provided, write the name of the numbered hormone-producing organ. Also name the hormone-producing organs described in numbers 11, 12, and 13.

A.

1. _____   6. _____

2. _____   7. _____

3. _____   8. _____

4. _____   9. _____

5. _____

B.

_____ 10. The posterior and anterior pituitaries hang from the bottom of this hormone-producing organ.

_____ 11. This is only present in pregnant women.

_____ 12. These are the four small glands attached to the thyroid.

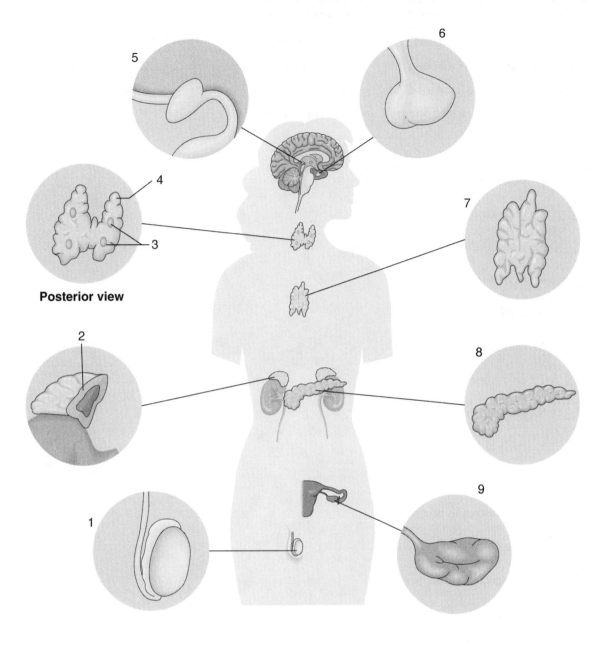

5

6

4

3

Posterior view

7

2

8

1

9

Fig. 5.23   The endocrine system

Matching: Using the following list of organs, match the organ with the hormone(s) it produces or releases and write the appropriate letter in the space provided.

A. adrenal gland (cortex) E. ovaries I. thyroid

B. adrenal gland (medulla) F. testes J. parathyroid

C. pituitary (anterior lobe) G. pancreas K. pineal

D. pituitary (posterior lobe) H. thymus

Hormones

_____ 1. prolactin

_____ 2. aldosterone

_____ 3. insulin

_____ 4. thyroxin

_____ 5. estrogen

_____ 6. cortisol

_____ 7. calcitonin

_____ 8. parathormone

_____ 9. ACTH

_____ 10. hydrocortisone

_____ 11. gonadotropic hormones

_____ 12. glucagon

_____ 13. triiodothyronine

_____ 14. oxytocin

_____ 15. progesterone

_____ 16. mineralocorticoids

_____ 17. epinephrine

_____ 18. TSH

_____ 19. testosterone

_____ 20. norepinephrine

_____ 21. growth hormone

_____ 22. corticosteroids

_____ 23. antidiuretic hormone

Matching: Match the term with the best description. Write the letter of the appropriate term next to the best description.

A. adrenocorticotropin
B. aldosterone
C. calcitonin
D. cortisol
E. estrogens
F. follicle-stimulating hormone
G. glucagon

H. insulin
I. lactogenic hormone
J. luteinizing hormone
K. oxytocin
L. parathormone
M. progesterone
N. TSH

_____ 1. antagonistic to insulin, produced by the same gland

_____ 2. promotes the lining of the uterus to thicken in preparation for fertilization

_____ 3. anterior pituitary hormones that regulate the female cycle

_____ 4. stimulates development of secretory parts of mammary glands

_____ 5. directly regulate the menstrual cycle

_____ 6. stimulates thyroid to produce thyroxin

_____ 7. decreases calcium in the blood

_____ 8. increases calcium level in the blood

_____ 9. stimulates mammary glands to secrete milk

_____ 10. helps protect the body during stress; stimulates the adrenal cortex

_____ 11. necessary for glucose to be taken up by cells

Identification: The following list of conditions are usually the result of hyper- or hypoactivity of an endrocine gland's production of a particular hormone. In the first column indicate whether the condition is due to hyper- or hypoactivity. In the second column write the name of the involved hormone.

_____ _____ 1. giantism

_____ _____ 2. Addison's disease

_____ _____ 3. Graves' disease

_____ _____ 4. masculinization; abnormal hairiness

_____ _____ 5. tetany

_____ _____ 6. slow heart rate, sluggish physical and mental activity

_____ _____ 7. spontaneous abortion

_____ _____ 8. acromegaly in an adult

_____ _____ 9. decalcification of bones making them brittle and prone to fracture

_____ _____ 10. high blood glucose; glucose in the urine

_____ _____ 11. Cushing's syndrome

_____ _____ 12. dwarfed stature and mental retardation (cretinism)

_____ _____ 13. failure of the reproductive organs to mature

Word Review: The student is encouraged to write down the meaning of each of the following words. The list can be used as a study guide for this unit.

adrenal glands	goiter	oxytocin
adrenocorticotropic hormone (ACTH)	gonadotropic hormones	pancreas
aldosterone	gonads	parathormone
antidiuretic hormone (ADH)	growth hormone	parathyroid glands
calcitonin	hormones	pituitary gland
cortisol	hyperactive	prolactin
diabetes mellitus	hypoactive	target organs
ducts	hypothalamus	testes
endocrine glands	insulin	testosterone
epinephrine	islets of Langerhans	tetany
estrogen	master gland	thyroid gland
exocrine glands	mineralocorticoids	thyroid stimulating hormone (TSH)
glucagon	norepinephrine	thyroxin
glucocorticoids	ovaries	triiodothyronine

System Seven: The Respiratory System

Identification: Identify the indicated structures in Figure 5.24. Write the correct letters next to the appropriate names in the space provided.

_____ 1. bronchus

_____ 2. roof of mouth

_____ 3. lower jawbone

_____ 4. epiglottis

_____ 5. larynx

_____ 6. lung

_____ 7. nasal passage

_____ 8. oral cavity

_____ 9. tongue

_____ 10. pulmonary vein

_____ 11. sinuses

_____ 12. pharynx

_____ 13. pulmonary artery

_____ 14. trachea

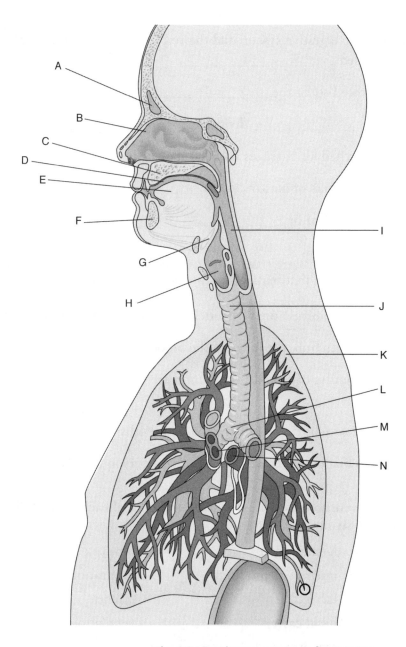

Fig. 5.24 Respiratory organs and structures

Completion: In the space provided, write the word or words that correctly completes each statement.

1. The exchange of oxygen and carbon dioxide that takes place in the body is called _____.

2. The exchange between the external environment and the blood that takes place in the lungs is termed _____.

3. The gaseous exchange between the blood and the cells of the body is termed _____.

4. The oxidation that occurs within the cell is termed _____.

5. Air enters the nasal cavity through the _____.

6. The function of the mucosa of the nasal cavity is to _____, _____, and _____ the air.

7. The passageway common to the digestive system and the respiratory system that is also referred to as the throat is called the _____.

8. The air passes through the voice box or the _____.

9. In the chest the wind pipe or _____ divides into two _____.

10. The entire system of multibranched air passages is called the _____.

11. The air passages terminate in clusters of air sacs called _____.

12. The act of ventilation is accomplished by _____.

True or False: If the following statements are true, write *true* in the space provided. If they are false, replace the italicized word with one that makes the statement true.

_____ 1. The blood in the pulmonary arteries has a high concentration of *oxygen*.

_____ 2. Oxygen moves from the lungs to the blood by *diffusion*.

_____ 3. The by-products of *internal respiration* are water, carbon dioxide, and energy.

_____ 4. *Carbon dioxide* is carried by the red blood cells in the blood.

_____ 5. When the diaphragm contracts, it causes a person to *exhale*.

Word Review: The student is encouraged to write down the meaning of each of the following words. The list can be used as a study guide for this unit.

alveoli	inhalation	pharynx
cellular respiration	internal respiration	respiration
diaphragm	larynx	trachea
exhalation	nasal cavity	ventilation
external respiration	oxidation	

System Eight: The Digestive System

Completion: In the space provided, write the word or words that correctly completes each statement.

1. The process of converting food into substances capable of nourishing cells is _____.

2. The process in which the digested nutrients are transferred from the intestines to the blood or lymph vessels to be transported to the cells is _____.

3. The muscular tube that goes from the lips to the anus is the _____ or the _____.

4. Organs that aid digestion but are located outside the digestive tract are known as _____ digestive organs.

5. The physical activity of digestion that takes place in the mouth is _____

6. The chemical digestive activity that takes place in the mouth is from secretions by the _____.

7. The physical or mechanical activity in the alimentary canal is from the action of the _____.

Identification: Identify the indicated structures in Figure 5.25. Write the correct names next to the appropriate numbers in the space provided.

1. _____
2. _____
3. _____
4. _____
5. _____
6. _____
7. _____
8. _____
9. _____
10. _____
11. _____
12. _____

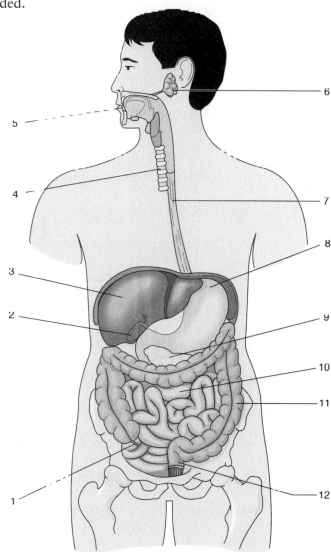

Fig. 5.25 The digestive system

Matching: Match the term with the best description. Write the letter of the appropriate term in the space provided.

A. bolus

B. cardiac sphincter

C. cecum

D. chyme

E. colon

F. duodenum

G. ileocecal valve

H. ileum

I. lacteals

J. mucosa

K. oral cavity

L. peristalsis

M. pyloric valve

N. rectum

O. saliva

P. serous layer

Q. submucosa

R. villa

_____ 1. beginning of the large intestine

_____ 2. contains enzymes that begin to break down carbohydrates

_____ 3. a mixture of digestive juices, mucous, and food material

_____ 4. a soft food ball that is swallowed

_____ 5. prevents movement from the large intestine to the small intestine

_____ 6. outer covering of the tube that is continuous with the peritoneum lining the abdominal cavity

_____ 7. rhythmic, wavelike, muscular motion

_____ 8. opening at the top of the stomach

_____ 9. temporary storage of solid waste

_____ 10. opening at the end of the stomach

_____ 11. a membrane made up of epithelial cells that carry on secretion and absorption

_____ 12. where food is masticated

_____ 13. plays an important role in determining how long food is held in the stomach

_____ 14. first section of small intestine

_____ 15. stores, forms, and excretes waste products; regulates the body's water balance

_____ 16. fingerlike projections that increase surface area of small intestines

_____ 17. organ that receives bile and pancreatic juices

_____ 18. lymph capillaries in the small intestine

_____ 19. serves to nourish the surrounding tissues and carry away the absorbed material

_____ 20. last section of small intestine

_____ 21. organ responsible for water absorption and feces formation

Word Review: The student is encouraged to write down the meaning of each of the following words. The list can be used as a study guide for this unit.

absorption	descending colon	pancreatic fluid
accessory digestive organs	digestion	peristalsis
alimentary canal	duodenum	pyloric sphincter
anal canal	feces	rectum
ascending colon	hydrochloric acid	saliva
bile	ileum	salivary glands
bolus	ileocecal valve	sigmoid colon
cardiac sphincter	intestinal digestive juices	small intestine
cecum	jejunum	transverse colon
chyme	lacteals	villi
colon	oral cavity	
common bile duct	pancreatic duct	

Matching: Match the term with the best description. Write the letter or letters of the appropriate excretory organ next to the term describing what that organ eliminates.

A. kidneys   C. liver   E. skin

B. large intestine   D. lungs

_____ 1. urine

_____ 2. food wastes

_____ 3. expiration

_____ 4. bile

_____ 5. uric acid

_____ 6. feces

_____ 7. urea

_____ 8. heat

_____ 9. CO_2

_____ 10. perspiration

_____ 11. water

Completion: In the space provided, write the word or words that correctly completes each statement.

1. The functional unit of the kidney is the _____.

2. The tubes that carry urine from the kidneys to the bladder are called _____.

3. A hormone produced in the kidneys that acts to regulate blood pressure is _____.

True or False: If the following statements are true, write *true* in the space provided. If they are false, replace the italicized word with one that makes the statement true.

_____ 1. The kidneys normally filter forty to fifty *gallons* of blood plasma a day.

_____ 2. When a person urinates, *voluntary* muscles in the walls of the bladder contract forcing the urine out of the body.

Identification: Identify the indicated structures in Figure 5.26. Write the correct names next to the appropriate numbers in the space provided.

1. _____
2. _____
3. _____
4. _____
5. _____

6. _____
7. _____
8. _____
9. _____

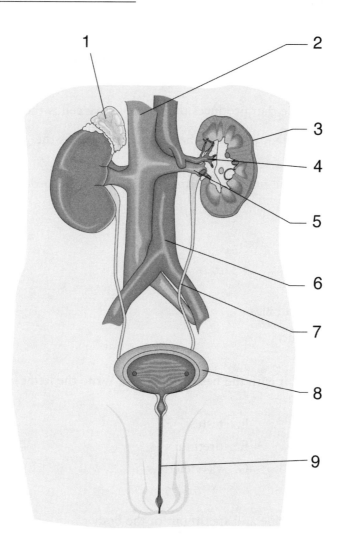

Fig. 5.26 The urinary system

Word Review: The student is encouraged to write down the meaning of each of the following words. The list can be used as a study guide for this unit.

bile	metabolic wastes	ureters
bladder	nephron	urethra
excretion	renin	urinary system

System Ten: The Human Reproductive System

Completion: In the space provided, write the word or words that correctly completes each statement.

1. One-celled organisms that do not need a partner to reproduce do so by nonsexual means called _____ reproduction.

2. The term used to describe a reproductive cell that can unite with another reproductive cell to form the cell that develops into a new individual is called a _____.

3. In males, the reproductive cells are called _____.

4. In females, the reproductive cells are called _____.

5. The cell formed by the union of the male and female reproductive cells is called a _____.

6. The gland in the female that produces the reproductive cell is the _____.

7. The gland in the male that produces the reproductive cell is the _____.

Short Answer: Number the following terms from 1 to 5 in the order that sperm would travel from the time it is produces until it leaves the body.

_____ vas deferens

_____ urethra

_____ epididymis

_____ seminiferous tubules

_____ ejaculatory ducts

Matching: Match the term with the best description. Write the letter of the appropriate term next to the best description.

A. Cowper's glands   E. testes
B. epididymis   F. urethra
C. prostate gland   G. vas deferens
D. seminal vesicles

_____ 1. conveys both urine and sperm out of the body

_____ 2. two convoluted, glandular tubes located on each side of the prostate gland

_____ 3. stores the sperm until it becomes fully mature

_____ 4. forms the male hormone testosterone

_____ 5. mucus producing glands that serve to lubricate the urethra

_____ 6. contains specialized cells that produce the spermatozoa

_____ 7. surrounds the first part of the urethra

_____ 8. two pea-sized glands located beneath the prostate gland

_____ 9. secrets an alkaline fluid that neutralizes the acidic vaginal secretions

_____ 10. secretions contain simple sugars, mucus, prostaglandin

_____ 11. two small, egg-shaped glands made up of minute convoluted tubules

_____ 12. sperm collects here until it is expelled from the body

_____ 13. located in the scrotum; receives sperm from the testes

Identification: Identify the indicated structures in Figure 5.27. Write the correct letter next to the appropriate name in the spaces provided.

_____ 1. bulbourethral gland

_____ 2. urethra

_____ 3. epididymis

_____ 4. erectile tissue

_____ 5. glans penis

_____ 6. prepuce

_____ 7. prostate gland

_____ 8. scrotum

_____ 9. seminal vesicle

_____ 10. testis

_____ 11. urinary bladder

_____ 12. vas deferens

_____ 13. spine

_____ 14. rectum

_____ 15. anal opening

_____ 16. ureter

_____ 17. symphysis pubis

_____ 18. spermatic cord

_____ 19. ejaculatory duct

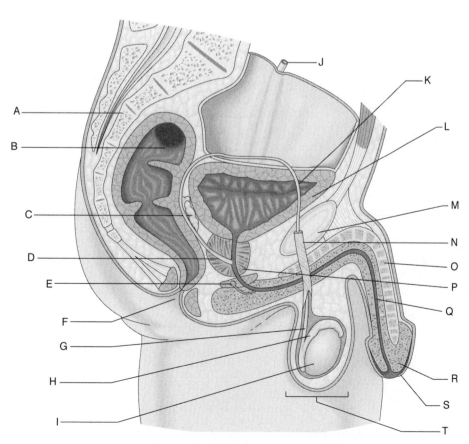

Fig. 5.27 The male reproductive system

Completion: In the space provided, write the word or words that correctly complete each statement.

1. The external part of the female reproductive system that includes the labia majora and the labia minora is termed the _____.

2. The muscular tube or canal that is the lower part of the birth canal is called the _____.

3. The chamber that houses the developing fetus is the _____.

4. The egg-carrying tubes of the female reproductive system are the _____.

5. The glands that produce estrogen and progesterone are the _____.

6. The egg cell capable of being fertilized by a spermatozoon is the _____.

Identification: Identify the indicated structures in Figure 5.28. Write the correct letter next to the appropriate terms in the space provided.

_____ 1. anal opening

_____ 2. cervix

_____ 3. fallopian tube

_____ 4. labium minora

_____ 5. labium majora

_____ 6. ovary

_____ 7. spine

_____ 8. rectum

_____ 9. symphysis pubis

_____ 10. urethra

_____ 11. urinary bladder

_____ 12. uterus

_____ 13. vagina

_____ 14. urinary opening

_____ 15. fundus of uterus

_____ 16. ureter

_____ 17. sacral promontory

_____ 18. posterior cul-de-sac

_____ 19. fornix of vagina

_____ 20. sacrouterine ligament

_____ 21. anterior cul-de-sac

_____ 22. crus of clitoris

_____ 23. urogenital diaphragm

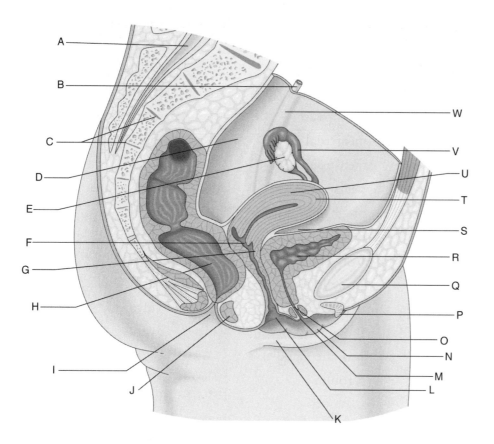

Fig. 5.28 The female reproductive system

Matching: Match the term with the best description. Write the letter of the appropriate term in the space provided.

A. corpus luteum   C. gestation   E. menstruation

B. estrogen   D. menopause   F. ovulation

_____ 1. controls the development of secondary female sexual characteristics

_____ 2. the release of the egg cell from the ovary

_____ 3. ovarian site of estrogen and progesterone production

_____ 4. occurs from the time an ovum is fertilized until childbirth

_____ 5. the cyclic uterine bleeding that normally occurs at about four-week intervals

_____ 6. follicle transformed by luteinizing hormone

_____ 7. the physiological cessation of the menstrual cycle

Word Review: The student is encouraged to write down the meaning of each of the following words. The list can be used as a study guide for this unit.

asexual reproduction	labia minora	semen
bulbourethral glands	luteinizing hormone	seminal fluid
cervix	menopause	seminal vesicles
corpus luteum	menstrual cycle	spermatozoa
ejaculatory ducts	menstruation	testes
epididymis	penis	testosterone
estrogen	pregnancy	urethra
fallopian tubes	ovary	uterus
fertilization	oviducts	vagina
fetus	ovulation	vas deferens
gamete	ovum	vulva
gestation	progesterone	zygote
gonad	prostate gland	
labia majora	scrotum	

MASSAGE PRACTICE

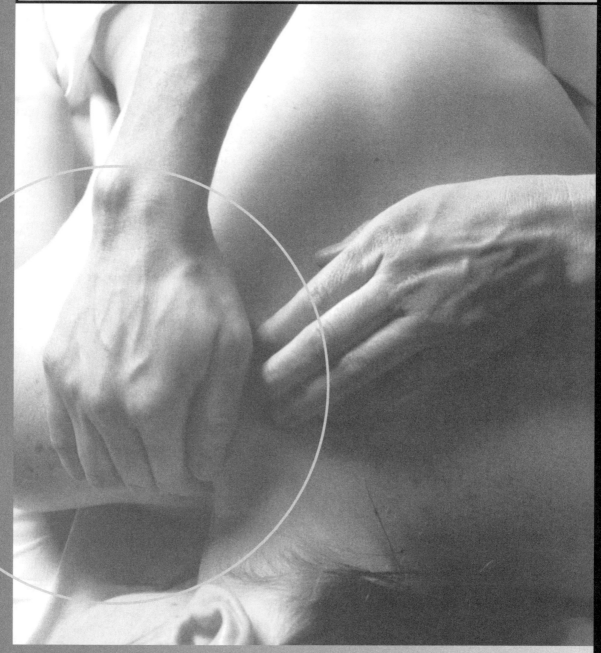

Effects, Benefits, Indications, and Contraindications of Massage

Completion: In the space provided write the word or words that correctly completes each statement.

1. A massage should not be given when ___Contraindication___ are present.

2. Direct physical effects of the massage techniques on the tissues are considered to be ___mechanical___ effects.

3. Indirect responses to touch that affect body functions and tissues through the nervous or energy systems are termed ___reflex___ effects.

4. Effects of massage on the structures of the body are considered ___physiological___ effects.

5. Mental and emotional effects of massage are ___psychological___ effects.

6. Any physical, emotional, or mental condition that may cause a particular massage treatment to be unsafe or detrimental to the client's well-being is a ___Contraindication___.

True or False: If the following statements are true, write *true* in the space provided. If they are false, replace the italicized word with one that makes the statement true.

___false___   1. Kneading and compression help to increase *circulation* ~~strength~~ in muscles.

___true___   2. *Active joint movements* increase strength, flexibility, and circulation.

Matching: Select the massage technique that is best described by the phrase. Place the letter(s) next to the appropriate description in the space provided.

A. active joint movements   D. friction   G. passive joint movement

B. compression   E. kneading   H. percussion

C. deep stroking   F. light stroking   I. vibration

D.   1. prevents and reduces excessive scarring following trauma

G.   2. rotation of joints through their range of motion with no resistance or assistance by muscular activity on the part of the client

B, C, F   3. relaxes and lengthens the muscles

D.   4. prevents and reduces the development of adhesions

A.   5. contraction of voluntary muscles are by the client, either resisted or assisted by the therapist

A.   6. helps to firm and strengthen muscles

F.   7. produces calming sedative effects

C, I   8. directed toward the heart in the direction of venous blood flow

D.   9. increases the permeability of the capillary beds and produces an increased flow of interstitial fluid

B, D   10. produces a hyperemia in the muscle tissue

Milady's Theory and Practice of Therapeutic Massage Workbook

106

Matching: Select the most appropriate answer(s) from the choices given. Write the letter(s) of the choice next to the appropriate description in the space provided.

  A. Avoid the affected area.

  B. Consult with the client's physician before proceeding.

  C. Do not perform the massage at this time.

  D. Massage specifically on the affected area.

  E. Proceed with a light noninvasive, soothing massage.

  F. Proceed with the massage as usual.

  G. Refer the client to a doctor.

C, G   1. Miss Harris is twenty-six years old and has been in to see you on a monthly basis. When she comes in for her regular appointment, she complains of a general achiness, is slightly flushed, and has a temperature of 101.5 degrees.

C, G   2. Mrs. Clements asks for you to come to her home to give her a massage. She says she would come to your office except that she has the flu.

A, G   3. Mr. James's wrist is red, swollen, and warm to the touch. He has come in for a general massage and asks you to pay particular attention to his wrist.

A, B, G   4. Mrs. Annest has come in for a massage. As she is getting on the table, you notice a red, flaky area on the inside of her elbow and another one on the back of her shoulder. When you ask, she says that they are "just some itchy patches she has had for a couple of weeks."

A F (G)   5. When Mr. Inkles lies face down on the table, you notice a number of inflamed bumps and pimples between his shoulder blades and on his shoulders.

B, E   6. Mr. Johnson, a forty-year-old, indicates that he is under a doctor's care for a condition that has caused a severe decalcification of the bones.

B, E   7. An eighty-three-year-old woman with noticeably stooped shoulders and somewhat deformed hands wants to start getting massages to help recover from a fractured hip she suffered three months ago.

A.   8. A thirty-five-year-old mother of three comes in for relief of sore feet and an achy lower back. When giving her a massage, you notice several bulging bluish masses on her legs.

A, B, F   9. A twenty-eight-year-old man comes into the clinic for a massage. He says that he was thrown from a horse two days before and has a lot of discomfort in his hip and thigh. When he gets on the table, you note a large black and blue area around his hip. He says he has gone to the doctor and x-rays determined there were no broken bones.

A, B, E   10. A thirty-five-year-old woman comes in for a massage. One week earlier she was in a car accident. No bones were broken, but she was shaken up pretty badly. She has large bruises on her upper arm and thigh that are still somewhat discolored.

_C, G_ 11. A woman who is seven months pregnant comes in and wants a massage because she is "stressed out." You notice that her hands and feet are somewhat swollen. When you press a finger into her ankle, it leaves a slight impression.

_C, G_ 12. Mr. Hill is fifty-four years old and is under a physician's care for high blood pressure. His physician has recommended massage as part of his treatment. You take his blood pressure when he comes for his massage and it is 170 over 130.

normal = 120 over 80   heart attack

_A, B, E_ 13. Mrs. Baird is forty-four years old and is in the middle of a series of chemo-therapy treatments after having a malignant growth removed from her colon. She is seeking massage for relief from stress and "to be good to herself."

_B, E_ 14. A forty-eight-year-old female executive is under a doctor's care for chronic fatigue and mental exhaustion. The doctor has recommended massage as part of her treatment.

CHAPTER 7

Equipment and Products

Completion: In the space provided, write the word or words that correctly completes each statement.

1. Professionalism is an _____.

2. As a massage practitioner, list at least four ways to project a professional image.

   a. _____   c. _____

   b. _____   d. _____

3. When operating a massage facility, two standards that must be maintained are_____ and _____.

4. The optimum temperature for a massage room is _____.

5. To assure an abundant supply of fresh air, a massage room should have good _____.

6. The lighting in a massage room should be _____.

7. A massage practitioner's most important piece of equipment is the _____.

8. Three attributes of a good massage table are that it is _____, _____, and _____.

9. In order to give the practitioner leverage and to prevent fatigue, the massage table must be _____.

10. A good width for a massage table is _____.

11. A good length for a massage table is _____.

12. One of a massage practitioner's most important supplies is the _____ they use on their clients.

13. If there is reason to believe the client is sensitive or allergic to a product or oil, the practitioner can perform a _____.

14. The three main areas of a massage business operation are the _____, the _____, and the_____.

CHAPTER 8

Sanitary and Safety Practices

Completion: In the space provided, write the word or words that correctly completes each statement.

1. In personal care services, the three levels of decontamination are _____, _____, and _____.

2. The removal of all living organisms on an object or surface, including bacterial spores, is _____.

3. Any item that comes in contact with the client must be clean and _____.

4. A massage practitioner's hands can be sanitized by _____.

5. Minute, unicellular microorganisms exhibiting both plant and animal characteristics are called _____.

6. Beneficial and harmless bacteria that perform useful functions are termed _____.

7. Bacteria that cause or produce disease are termed _____.

8. Three general forms of pathogenic bacteria are _____, _____, and _____.

9. The body's natural ability to resist infection is _____.

10. The body's most important defense against invasion of harmful bacteria is the _____.

11. A class of proteins produced in the body in response to contact with an invading bacteria is an _____.

12. Microscopic pathogenic agents that invade living cells and are capable of transmitting disease are called _____.

13. The primary precaution in infection control is thorough _____.

14. An acceptable way to sanitize linens is to wash them in water and add one-fourth to one-half cup of _____.

15. Floors, sinks, and restrooms can be cleaned and sanitized with a solution of

    _____.

16. A common disinfectant used to clean surfaces and implements is a _____ percent chlorine bleach solution.

17. If there is suspicion of bacterial contamination, the hands can be rinsed with

    _____.

Short Answer: In the space provided, write a short answer to the following questions.

1. If a client has an infection or contagious disease, what are two things the massage practitioner should do?

   a. _____

   b. _____

2. When should the massage practitioner wash their hands?

   _____

3. List three acceptable means of sanitizing implements.

   a. _____

   b. _____

   c. _____

4. List three agents that can be used to disinfect implements.

   a. _____

   b. _____

   c. _____

Matching: Match the methods of disinfecting or sterilization with the given situation. Write the letter or letters of the appropriate procedure in the space provided.

A. boiling in water   E. rinsing with alcohol solution

B. chlorine bleach   F. soap and hot water

C. creosol or Lysol™   G. wiping with alcohol

D. immersing in quats

_____ 1. massage table surface with normal use

_____ 2. massage table face cradle

_____ 3. practitioner's hands before a massage

_____ 4. practitioner's hands after a massage

_____ 5. practitioner's hands after working on client with possible contagious skin condition

_____ 6. bathroom sink

_____ 7. bathroom floor

_____ 8. shower stall

_____ 9. linens after normal use

_____ 10. linens after use on client with possible contagious condition

_____ 11. brushes and combs kept for client use

_____ 12. towels used for wraps and hydrotherapy

_____ 13. fever thermometer before use

_____ 14. fever thermometer after use

CHAPTER 9

The Consultation

Completion: In the space provided, write the word or words that correctly completes each statement.

1. A meeting between the prospective client and the practitioner where views are discussed and valuable information is exchanged is called a _Consultation_.

2. In order for a consultation to be effective, there must be clear _Communication_ between the client and the practitioner.

3. The two most effective ways for the practitioner to ask questions of the client are _verbally_ and _written_.

Short Answer: In the space provided, write a short answer to the following questions.

1. List six things the therapist can accomplish during the consultation.

   a. _greet the client and introduce himself or herself._

   b. _determine the clients needs and expectations._

   c. _explain procedures_

   d. _state policies_

   e. _preform preliminary assesment_

   f. _formulate a treatment plan._

2. When making a first appointment with a prospective client, what are three questions that can be asked in order to screen them?

   a. _have you had a massage before?_

   b. _how did you find out about my services_

   c. _what is your main reason for making this appt?_

3. List four areas that a practitioner may include in a policy statement.

    a. missed or late appointments

    b. payment of fees

    c. sexual boundaries (clearly stated)

    d. not a medical treatment

4. Three reasons to perform a preliminary assessment are to:

    a. Client history

    b. Observation

    c. examination

Completion: In the space provided, write the word or words that correctly completes each statement.

1. To help disclose problems and the physiological basis for the client's complaints, an assessment includes _____, _____, and _____.

2. Information gained from intake and medical forms, answers to questions, and descriptions the client offers are the basis for the _____.

3. Noticing how clients hold their bodies, how they move, and how they react to questions or manipulative tests is part of _____.

4. Various manipulative and verbal tests that help determine more precisely the tissues or conditions involved are part of the _____.

5. The outline a practitioner develops and follows when giving massage treatments is termed a _____.

Short Answer: In the space provided, write a short answer to the following questions.

1. List four sources of information used when formulating a treatment plan.

    a. _____

    b. _____

    c. _____

    d. _____

2. List the kind of information that is kept in the client files.

    a. release form

    b. _____

    c. _____

    d. _____

3. What information does a practitioner record in a treatment record?

   a. _subjective_

   b. _objective_

   c. _assessment_

   d. _planning_

Completion: In the space provided, write the word or words that correctly completes each statement.

1. During a consultation, if the client appears flushed, unusually warm, and does not feel well, then it is best to take his or her _____ and _____.

2. A marked elevation in body temperature tends to increase the _____.

3. The average resting pulse rate of an adult is between ___70-80___ beats per minute.

4. The pulse rate is the number of beats counted in ___15___ seconds and multiplied by 4 (or 60 seconds).

5. The most common area to palpate for the pulse is the _____ .

6. Normal temperature is about ___98.6___.

7. An abnormally high pulse or body temperature is a _____ for massage.

8. The acronym in the term "SOAP charting" stands for ___sub___, ___ob.___, ___assessment___, and ___plan___.

Classification of Massage Movements

Completion: In the space provided, write the word or words that correctly complete each statement.

1. Three physical factors that control the results of a manipulation are the _duration_, _pressure_, and _direction_ of the movement.

2. Another important factor that affects the outcome of a technique or massage is the _intention_ with which it is given.

3. In Swedish massage most movements are directed _toward_ the heart.

4. Massage strokes are directed toward the heart in order to affect the flow of _Venus blood_ and _lymph_.

5. The six major categories of massage movements are _touching_, _gliding_, _kneading_, _friction_, _joint movement_ and _percussion_.

Identification: Name the classification of massage manipulation described in each statement. Write the correct classification next to the appropriate description in the space provided.

gliding   1. applied in the direction of the venous and lymphatic flow

kneading   2. lifts, squeezes, and presses the tissues

gliding   3. used to distribute any lubricant and to prepare the area for other techniques

joint movement   4. manipulation of the articulations of the client

touch   5. generally the first and last contact the practitioner has with the client

touch   6. placing of the practitioner's hand or fingers on the client without movement in any direction

percussion   7. rapid striking motion against the surface of the client's body _____friction_____ 8. moving more superficial layers of flesh against the deeper tissues

_____joint movement_____ 9. moving a body part through a range of motion

_____touch_____ 10. the stationary contact of the practitioner's hand and the client's body

_____gliding_____ 11. moving the hand over some portion of the client's body with varying amounts of pressure

_____joint movement_____ 12. used to assist a client to restore mobility or increase flexibility in a joint

_____kneading_____ 13. raising tissues from their ordinary position and then squeezing, rolling, or pinching with firm pressure

_____friction_____ 14. manipulating one layer of tissue over or against another

Matching: Touch and gliding techniques can be further classified as superficial or deep. In the space provided write the letter or letters of the most appropriate techniques next to the description.

A. superficial touch   C. superficial gliding
B. deep touch   D. deep gliding

_____A,C_____ 1. Client has moderately high blood pressure.

_____A,C_____ 2. Client is nervous and irritated.

_____A,C_____ 3. Client is in pain from severe arthritis.

_____D_____ 4. Client is healthy with thick, heavy musculature.

_____B_____ 5. Client has trigger points in the neck and shoulders.

_____don't do_____ 6. Client is critically ill with lymphoma.

_____B_____ 7. Client has stress points in the tendons around the elbow and knee.

_____C_____ 8. Client complains of insomnia.

_____B_____ 9. This is the main technique used in foot reflexology.

_____C_____ 10. This technique is used when applying oil to the body.

_____D_____ 11. Client requests a deep relaxing massage.

_____B_____ 12. This is the main technique used in shiatsu.

_____C_____ 13. Client is generally tired.

_____A,C_____ 14. Client is visibly nervous and tense.

117

Matching: Match the terms with the best description. Write the letter of the best description in the space provided.

___E___ 1. hacking

___L___ 2. skin rolling

___R___ 3. aura stroking

___F___ 4. active, assistive joint movements

___M___ 5. superficial gliding

___C___ 6. cross-fiber friction

___N___ 7. kneading

___J___ 8. friction

___D___ 9. superficial touch

___G___ 10. circular friction

___O___ 11. tapping

___Q___ 12. active, resistive joint movements

___I___ 13. feather stroking

___A___ 14. compression

___K___ 15. deep touch

___P___ 16. passive joint movements

___B___ 17. deep gliding

___H___ 18. vibration

A. rhythmic pumping action directed into the muscle perpendicular to the body part

B. a stroke with enough pressure to have a mechanical effect

C. applied in a transverse direction across the muscle, tendon, or ligament fibers

D. the natural weight of the practitioner's finger, fingers, or hand held on a given area of the client's body

E. quick, striking manipulations with ulnar border of the hand

F. help from the practitioner as the client moves a limb

G. moving the skin in a circular pattern over the deeper tissues

H. a continuous shaking or trembling movement transmitted from the practitioner's hand or an electrical appliance

I. very light fingertip pressure with long, flowing strokes

J. moving more superficial layers of flesh against deeper tissues

K. applying pressure with no other movement

L. picking the skin and subcutaneous tissue up between the thumbs and fingers and rolling

M. moving a flexible, firm hand lightly over extended area of the body

N. raising the skin and muscular tissues from their ordinary position and squeezing with a firm pressure, usually in a circular direction

Q. quick, striking manipulations with tips of the fingers

R. moving a client's joint while their muscles are relaxed

Q. the practitioner's resistance of a client's movement

R. hands gliding over a body part without touching

True or False: If the following statements are true, write *true* in the space provided. If they are false, replace the italicized word with one that makes the statement true.

centrifugal   1. Massage strokes directed away from the heart are termed *centripetal*.

stimulating   2. In order to have a *sedating* effect, the rhythm of the massage must be steady and slightly faster than the client's natural rhythm.

pain   3. A primary indication of tension and dysfunction in soft tissue is *numbness*.

true   4. The pressure used with a massage technique should start out light, then increase and end *light*.

w/ caution   5. Deep massage techniques that cause a client to react in pain must be *avoided*.

CHAPTER 11

Application of Massage Technique

Completion: In the space provided, write the word or words that correctly completes each statement.

1. The primary tools the practitioner uses when giving a massage are the _____.

2. The practitioner conserves energy and increases power in massage movements by using his or her _____.

3. The observation of body postures in relation to safe and efficient body movement is called _____.

4. To increase strength and power and at the same time reduce the chance of fatigue and injury, the practitioner must use _____.

5. The risk of injury to the body is directly proportionate to the amount of stress and the amount of _____.

6. The Chinese term for the body's geographical center is the _____.

7. The state of self-assurance, balance, and emotional stability is often referred to as being _____.

8. The concept that the practitioner functions as a conduit or conductor allowing negative energies to pass out of the client and positive energies to flow in is known as _____.

9. The most common stances for the practitioner while performing a massage are called _____.

10. The stance in which both feet are placed in line with the edge of the table is called the _____.

11. The most commonly used stance is _____.

12. An exercise that helps the practitioner reach the full length of a client's body part while shifting weight on the feet and maintaining good posture and balance is called _____.

13. An exercise in which one imagines turning a large wheel is called _____.

14. An exercise that involves a powerful forward movement followed by a controlled with-drawal is called _____.

15. The exercise that emphasizes the importance of posture, concentration, centering, ground-ing, and correct breathing is called _____.

Short Answer: Write short answers to the following questions or statements in the spaces provided.

1. When practicing most massage techniques, where should the practitioner's hands be?

   _____

2. In what way does the practitioner apply deeper pressure or more force to a movement?

   _____

3. Why is it important to the practitioner not to raise and tighten the shoulders when giving a massage?

   _____

4. List seven advantages of using good body mechanics and proper stances when giving massages.

   a. _____

   _____

   b. _____

   c. _____

   _____

   d. _____

   e. _____

   _____

   f. _____

   _____

   g. _____

Short Answer: Provide short answers to the following questions. Write your answers in the space provided.

1. When should the practitioner wash their hands?

   _____

2. List four ways to avoid chilling the client.

   a. _____

   b. _____

   c. _____

   d _____

3. In what direction should gliding movements be given?

   _____

4. Why should extremely heavy or jarring movements be avoided?

   _____

Procedures for Complete Body Massages

Short Answer: Provide short answers to the following questions. Write your answers in the space provided.

1. What is the purpose of explaining your general procedures to clients on their first visit?

   a. _____

   b. _____

2. Ideally, what clothing should a client wear when getting a massage?

   _____

3. How can the practitioner dispel anxiety the client may have about nudity?

   _____

   _____

4. Why should the practitioner assist the client on and off of the table?

   _____

5. How can the practitioner assure that the client assumes the correct position on the table?

   _____

6. What can be done if a client cannot lie down for a massage?

   _____

Completion: In the space provided, write the word or words that correctly completes each statement.

1. The procedure used to assure a client's warmth and sense of modesty is called _____.

2. The implement used to support a client who cannot comfortably lie flat on the table is a _____.

3. The process of using linens to keep a client covered while performing a massage is called _____.

Short Answer: Provide short answers to the following questions. Write your answers in the space provided.

1. What are three advantages of draping to clients?

   a. _____

   b. _____

   c. _____

2. What advantage does draping offer the practitioner?

   _____

   _____

3. What is a good temperature for a massage room?

   _____

4. For those times when the massage room is slightly cool, name two things the practitioner can use to assure the client's warmth.

   a. _____

   b. _____

5. When using proper draping procedures, what part of the client's body is uncovered?

   _____

6. List three types of draping and the linens required for each.

   a. _____

   b. _____

   c. _____

Short Answer: Provide short answers to the following questions. Write your answers in the space provided.

1. In order to get from the dressing area or hydrotherapy area to the massage table, what covering does the client use to maintain modesty:

   a. when using the diaper draping method?

   _____

   b. when using top sheet draping?

   _____

   c. when using single sheet draping?

   _____

Short Answer: Provide short answers to the following questions. Write your answers in the space provided.

1. The client uses a wrap or towel to get from the dressing area to the massage table. What size should it be?

   _____

   _____

2. Where should the opening on the wrap be located?

   _____

3. List three reasons it is important to maintain contact with the client once it is established.

   a. _____

   _____

   b. _____

   _____

   c. _____

   _____

Short Answer: Provide short answers to the following questions. Write your answers in the space provided.

1. What are two important objectives of a good massage sequence?

   a. _____

   b. _____

2. When considering a sequence for a full body massage, what are two primary considerations?

   a. _____

   b. _____

3. Arrange the following body parts into a sequence for a massage. Begin with the right hand and successively number the body parts in the order they would be massaged.

_____	back	_____	neck (face up)
_____	face	_____	right arm
_____	left arm	_____	right foot
_____	left foot	_____	right hand
_____	left hand	_____	right leg (back)
_____	left leg (back)	_____	right leg (front)
_____	left leg (front)	_____	torso

4. Arrange the following body parts into a sequence for a massage. Begin with the left foot and successively number the body parts in the order they would be massaged.

_____	back	_____	right hand
_____	left arm	_____	right arm
_____	left foot	_____	right foot
_____	left hand	_____	right leg (back)
_____	left leg (back)	_____	light leg (front)
_____	left leg (front)	_____	torso
_____	neck (face up)		

5. Arrange the following body parts into a sequence for a massage of the front of the body. Begin with the face and finish the front of the body by massaging the torso. Successively number the body parts in the order they would be massaged.

_____	face	_____	right arm
_____	left arm	_____	right foot
_____	left foot	_____	right hand
_____	left hand	_____	right leg
_____	left leg	_____	torso
_____	neck		

6. Arrange the following body parts into a sequence for a massage of the front of the body. Begin with the right arm and finish the front of the body by massaging the left foot. Number the body parts in the order they would be massaged.

_____	face	_____	right arm
_____	left arm	_____	right foot
_____	left foot	_____	right hand
_____	left hand	_____	right leg
_____	left leg	_____	torso
_____	neck		

Key Choices: In the following sequence of movements for a body part, fill in the spaces with the most appropriate choices from the following list of movements.

effleurage   friction movements   petrissage

feather strokes   joint movements

1. apply the oil   6. effleurage

2. _____   7. _____

3. _____   8. effleurage

4. effleurage   9. _____

5. _____   10. redrape

Short Answer: Provide short answers to the following questions. Write your answers in the space provided.

1. In Swedish style massage an oil or lubricant is used. Describe the three-step procedure for applying the lubricant from its container to the client's body.

   a. _____

   b. _____

   c. _____

2. How is contact with the client maintained when preparing to apply a lubricant?

   _____

   _____

3. What massage strokes are directed toward the heart?

   _____

4. What strokes can be directed away from the heart?

   _____

5. Why are strokes directed toward the heart?

   _____

6. What part of the hand is used to apply gliding strokes to larger areas of the body?

   _____

7. Why follow deep friction movements with gliding strokes?

   _____

8. What is the first massage technique used after the oil is applied to a body part?

   _____

9. What preliminary steps should be taken before a client arrives for a massage?

   _____

   _____

10. How should the client be greeted?

_____

11. When should an information form be filled out?

_____

Short Answer: Provide short answers to the following questions. Write your answers in the space provided.

1. Name three areas of the body where lubricant is usually not needed.

_____

2. Why are gliding strokes repeated between other massage strokes?

_____

3. How many gliding strokes are usually applied between other strokes in a general massage?

_____

4. When applying gliding strokes to the arm, in which direction is pressure applied?

_____

5. When applying long gliding strokes to the leg with both hands, which hand leads?

_____

6. What does the acronym ASIS stand for?

_____

7. When extending the leg during joint movements, why is it important to keep one hand behind the knee?

_____

8. What is the massage technique most likely to increase muscle length and increase range of motion?

_____

9. What special consideration must be given when massaging a woman's torso?

_____

10. When working on the abdomen, what is the general direction of the massage movements?

_____

11. What is the "caring stroke"?

_____

12. What are the lightest gliding strokes using only the finger tips?

_____

Short Answer: Provide short answers to the following questions. Write your answers in the space provided.

1. Why is a client encouraged to drink plenty of water following massage?

   _____

2. How much water is suggested to drink per day?

   _____

3. Client's sometimes feel adverse aftereffects following massage. What are four possible adverse aftereffects?

   a. _____

   b. _____

   c. _____

   d. _____

4. What is thought to be the cause of these side effects?

   _____

Completion: In the space provided, write the word or words that correctly completes each statement.

1. The four steps of a therapeutic procedure are _____, _____, _____, and _____.

2. Reviewing any information available at the onset of the process takes place during the _____ stage of the therapeutic procedure.

3. Determining strategies and selecting therapeutic techniques to address specific conditions takes place during the _____ stage of the therapeutic procedure.

4. Examining the outcome of the session in regard to the effectiveness of the selected procedure for the condition takes place during the _____ stage of the therapeutic procedure.

5. Recording the client history, examination, and observation takes place during the _____ stage of the therapeutic procedure.

Short Answer: Provide short answers to the following questions. Write your answers in the space provided.

1. What are two methods of obtaining a client history?

   _____

2. When does the observation portion of an assessment begin?

   _____

3. What are three things a therapist can watch for while observing a client?

   a. _____

   b. _____

   c. _____

4. During the observation phase of an assessment, what does bilateral symmetry refer to?

   _____

Completion: In the space provided, write the word or words that correctly completes each statement.

1. Structural deviations, such as a tilted head, rotated hips, or a raised shoulder, are often the result of _____.

2. Posture is best observed when a person is _____ and is best done from _____ sides.

3. The action of a joint through the entire extent of its movement is called _____.

4. Three modes used in assessing the quality of this movement are _____, _____, and _____ movement.

5. The English osteopath who developed a system of testing joints and soft tissue lesions was _____.

6. According to his definition, fibrous tissues that have tensions placed on them during muscular contractions are called _____.

7. Tissues that are not contractile, such as bone, ligament, bursa, blood vessels, nerves, nerve coverings, and cartilage, are _____.

8. The quality of the sensation the therapist feels as they passively move a joint to the full extent of its possible range is termed_____.

9. The results of testing that the therapist is able to see or feel are called _____.

10. The results of tests that the client feels, such as pain or discomfort, and the way the client reacts to the discomfort are considered to be _____ findings.

11. When assessing _____ movement, the client moves through a particular range of motion totally unassisted.

12. It is termed _____ when the practitioner moves the client's joint through full range of motion while the client remains relaxed.

Short Answer: Provide short answers to the following questions. Write your answers in the space provided.

1. When testing range of motion, which side should be tested first?

   _____

2. In what order should the three modes of testing range of motion be performed?

   a. _____

   b. _____

   c. _____

3. What tissues are involved during active movement?

   _____

4. If there is pain during active movement, what are four things the therapist should note?

   a. _____

   b. _____

   c. _____

   d. _____

5. If there is a limitation to the movement during active movement, what are two things the therapist should note?

   a. _____

   b. _____

Completion: In the space provided, write the word or words that correctly completes each statement.

1. There are three types of end feel considered normal. An abrupt, painless limitation to further movement that happens at the normal end of the range of motion, such as knee or elbow extension, is called _____ end feel.

2. A cushioned limitation where soft tissue prevents further movement, such as knee or elbow flexion, is called _____ end feel.

3. It is called _____ end feel, when the limitation is caused by the stretch of fibrous tissue as the joint reaches the extent of its range of motion.

4. Normal end feel happens at the _____ of a normal range of motion and is _____.

5. Sudden pain during passive movement before the end of normal range of motion was termed _____ by Cyriax.

6. Abnormal end feel is indicated during passive movement when there is _____ or _____ in the movement.

7. Passive movement assessment indicates the condition of the _____ tissues.

8. Full, painless passive range of motion indicates that the joint and associated structures are _____.

9. Two indicators of dysfunction are _____ and _____

10. Resisted or isometric movement is used to assess the condition of the _____ tissues.

11. Indicators of lesions or dysfunction in the contractile tissue are _____ and _____.

12. Another name for resisted or isometric movement assessment is _____.

13. Sensing the difference in tissue quality and integrity through touch is termed _____.

14. A common palpable condition found in muscle that is usually associated with a lesion is a fibrous or _____ band.

15. Examining the outcome of the process in relation to the expected objectives is called _____.

True or False: If the following statements are true, write *true* in the space provided. If they are false, replace the italicized word with one that makes the statement true.

_____ 1. Palpation is most effective when used in conjunction with and *before* assessing range of motion.

_____ 2. When *passive* movement and resisted movement both give positive results, contractile tissues are involved.

_____ 3. A *strong* and painful muscle test indicates a lesion in the inert tissue, possibly a torn ligament or fracture.

_____ 4. The more severe the condition, the more severe the *pain*.

_____ 5. *Taut bands* usually contain trigger points.

Short Answer: Provide short answers to the following questions. Write your answers in the space provided.

1. What information is used in developing session strategies?

_____

_____

2. What takes place during the performance phase of the therapeutic procedure?

_____

_____

CHAPTER 13

Face and Scalp Massage

Completion: In the space provided, write the word or words that correctly completes each statement.

1. A professional who specializes in facials and skin care is called an _____.

2. The first important step in a face massage is _____ the face.

3. The five classifications of manipulations used for face massage are _____, _____, _____, _____, and _____.

Short Answer: Provide short answers to the following questions. Write your answers in the space provided.

1. When is it determined whether or not to give a face massage?

   _____

2. What products are used for cleansing the face before a massage?

   a. _____

   b. _____

   c. _____

   d. _____

3. What amount of cleansing cream or lotion is used to cleanse the face?

   _____

4. What is used to remove the cleansing product from the face?

   _____

5. Generally, in what direction are the strokes made when removing the cleansing product?

   _____

Short Answer: Provide short answers to the following questions. Write your answers in the space provided.

1. When giving a scalp massage, in what direction are the strokes applied?

   _____

2. What precaution should be observed during scalp massage?

   _____

3. When should scalp massage be avoided?

   _____

Hydrotherapy

Completion: In the space provided, write the word or words that correctly completes each statement.

1. Overexposure to the sun is dangerous to the skin because _ultraviolet rays_ penetrate the epidermis and affect the living cells of the _dermis_.

2. The skin's main defense against too much sun is to _tan_.

3. Tanning occurs when ultraviolet rays react with _melanin_ and cause it to darken.

4. One of the primary causes of skin cancer is _ultraviolet_.

5. The sun reacts with the skin to produce vitamin _D._.

6. Ultraviolet light therapy is an accepted treatment for the skin condition known as _acne_.

Completion: In the space provided, write the word or words that correctly completes each statement.

1. The use of heat and cold is a powerful therapeutic agent because the physiological effects are _____.

2. The short application of cold is _____ while prolonged application of cold _____ metabolic activity.

3. The local application of heat causes the blood vessels to _____ and circulation to _____.

4. The application of heat causes the pulse rate to _____ and the white blood cell count to _____.

5. A generalized lowering of the body temperature is termed _____.

Key Choices: The following is a list of reactions to hydrotherapy. Put the appropriate letter(s) in the spaces provided for each of the following conditions.

C = Cold Application

H = Heat Application

C _____ 1. hypothermia

C _____ 2. vasodilation

C _____ 3. reduced circulation

H _____ 4. anesthetic effect

H _____ 5. increased circulation

C _____ 6. increased perspiration

H _____ 7. numbness

M _____ 8. increased white cell count

H _____ 9. local muscle relaxation

C _____ 10. analgesia

H _____ 11. depressed metabolic activity

H _____ 12. reduced nerve sensitivity

C _____ 13. hyperthermia

H _____ 14. decreased muscle spasticity

C _____ 15. leukocyte migration into the area

True or False: If the following statements are true, write *true* in the space provided. If they are false, replace the italicized word with one that makes the statement true.

true _____ 1. People with very *thin* skin are more prone to spotting, freckling, and skin cancer.

physical _____ 2. When heat or cold is applied to the body, certain *physiological* changes occur.

true _____ 3. A *short* application of cold sedates metabolic activity.

true _____ 4. The warming effect of the sun is due to *ultraviolet* rays.

true _____ 5. The application of *cold* to a fresh soft-tissue injury will reduce pain and swelling.

Completion: In the space provided, write the word or words that correctly completes each statement.

1. When a body part is submerged in water, it is called a(n) _bath_.

2. The application of cold agents for therapeutic purposes is termed _____.

3. The application of water to the body for therapeutic purposes is known as _____.

4. The changes produced by water that is above or below body temperature are considered to be _____ effects.

5. The upper temperature limit for water that is considered safe for therapeutic purposes is _____.

6. The normal temperature of the body is __95.6°F__ or _____.

7. The body's normal skin surface temperature is approximately _____

8. A bath where only the hips and pelvis is submerged is called a _____.

Short Answer: Provide short answers to the following questions. Write your answers in the space provided.

1. List four variables that determine the nature and extent of the effects of heat or cold on the body.

   a. _stimulating_

   b. _depress metabolic activity_

   c. _damage tissue_

   d. _fever like reaction_

2. What are the three forms in which water is used for therapeutic purposes?

   a. _____

   b. _____

   c. _____

3. What are the properties of water that make it a valuable therapeutic agent?

   a. _____

   b. _____

   c. _____

4. The three classifications of therapeutic effects of water on the body are:

   a. _____

   b. _____

   c. _____

5. List three ways of applying moist heat.

   a. bath

   b. spray

   c. sponging

6. The acronym RICE stands for

   a. r - rest

   b. i - ice.

   c. c - compression

   d. e - elevation

7. List three economical methods of applying local cold therapy.

   a. ice bath

   b. wrap ice in a towl

   c. frozen (as if en ice pop)

8. List the three normal reactions to ice therapy in the order in which they occur.

   a. skin is chilled

   b. surface blood vessels contract

   c. nerve sensitivity is reduced

9. Baths can be classified according to the temperature of the water. What is the temperature range for the following baths?

   a. cold bath — 40 to 65 °F

   b. tepid bath — 85 to 95 °F

   c. warm bath — 95 to 100 °F

   d. hot bath — 100 to 115 °F

   e. steam bath — _____ to _____ °F

CHAPTER 15

Massage for Nursing and Healthcare

Short Answer: Provide short answers to the following questions. Write your answers in the space provided.

1. What massage system is most frequently used in nursing?

   _____

2. What basic manipulations are most frequently used in nursing?

   _____

3. What is the general goal of using massage in nursing and healthcare?

   _____

4. What is the main difference between nurses who use massage and massage practitioners?

   _____

   _____

   _____

Short Answer: Provide short answers to the following questions. Write your answers in the space provided.

1. List at least two ways that massage benefits the skin.

   a. _____

   b. _____

2. List three ways that massage benefits the muscular system.

   a. _____

   b. _____

   c. _____

3. List five ways that massage benefits the nervous system.

    a. _____

    b. _____

    c. _____

    d. _____

    e. _____

4. List at least three ways that massage benefits the circulatory system.

    a. _____

    b. _____

    c. _____

    d. _____

    e. _____

Short Answer: Provide short answers to the following questions. Write your answers in the space provided.

1. In what direction are effleurage movements given?

    _____

2. What does it mean that effleurage strokes are centripetal?

    _____

3. Manipulations involving the movement of the superficial tissues over or against the deeper tissues are called _____.

4. What preliminary precautions should be taken when massage is administered in cases where there is injury or illness?

    _____

5. What are seven warning signs of cancer?

    a. _____

    b. _____

    c. _____

    d. _____

    e. _____

    f. _____

    g. _____

6. When a massage is given to a person in a hospital bed, what are two adjustments that can be made to improve the delivery of the massage?

a. _____

b. _____

CHAPTER 16

Athletic/Sports Massage

Completion: In the space provided, write the word or words that correctly completes each statement.

1. The 1972 Olympic gold medalist who was known as "the flying Finn" and who credited daily massage for his success was _____.

2. The application of massage techniques that combine sound anatomical and physiological knowledge, an understanding of strength training and conditioning, and specific massage skills to enhance athletic performance is termed _____ or _____.

3. The study of body movement is termed _____.

4. In sports physiology the _____ principle states that in order to improve either strength or endurance, appropriate stresses must be applied to the system.

5. If the intensity of the athletic training exceeds the body's ability to recuperate, the result will probably be _____.

6. The rhythmic pumping massage manipulation that is applied to the belly of the muscle is called _____.

7. Increasing the amount of blood available in a body area is called _____.

8. If pressure on a tender point causes pain to radiate or refer to another area of the body, that point is considered a _____.

9. The massage technique most often used on trigger points is _____.

10. The amount of pressure a therapist uses on a trigger point is determined by the _____.

11. _____ is applied by rubbing across the fibers of the tendon, muscle, or ligament at a 90° angle to the fibers.

12. The British osteopath who popularized cross-fiber friction is _____.

Short Answer: Provide short answers to the following questions. Write your answers in the space provided.

1. Why does athletic massage enable athletes to participate more often in rigorous physical training and conditioning?

   _____

2. How does athletic massage reduce the chance of injury?

   _____

3. List four negative effects of exercise.

   a. _____

   b. _____

   c. _____

   d. _____

4. How long does it normally take for a muscle that has been stressed to the point of fatigue to recuperate?

   _____

5. What are two important effects of compression strokes?

   a. _____

   b. _____

6. In what direction is cross-fiber friction given?

   _____

7. How long is a cross-fiber stroke?

   _____

   _____

8. What does the acronym PNF stand for?

   _____

Key Choices: Choose the massage technique that best fits the description or is most likely to produce the following effects. Write the appropriate letter next to the description or effect.

A. compression   C. cross-fiber friction

B. deep pressure   D. active joint movement

_____ 1. softens adhesions in fibrous tissue

_____ 2. causes increased amounts of blood to remain in the muscle over an extended period of time

_____ 3. reduces fibrosis

_____ 4. adopted from proprioceptive neuromuscular facilitation

_____ 5. rubbing across the fibers of the tendon, muscle, or ligament

_____ 6. used effectively to treat tender points

_____ 7. arhythmic pumping action to the belly of the muscle

_____ 8. therapist supports the body part in position while the client contracts his or her muscles

_____ 9. promotes increased circulation deep in the muscle

_____ 10. reducing the crystalline roughness that forms between tendons and their sheaths

_____ 11. helps to counteract muscle spasm, improve flexibility, and restore muscle strength

_____ 12. creates hyperemia in the muscle tissue

_____ 13. deactivates trigger points and increases function to the referred area

_____ 14. based on Sherington's physiological principles

_____ 15. stretches, broadens, and separates muscle fibers

_____ 16. encourages the formation of strong, pliable scar tissue at the site of healing injuries

_____ 17. based on reciprocal inhibition and post-isometric relaxation

Key Choices: Choose the athletic massage application that best fits the description. Write the letter of the application next to the description in the space provided.

A = Post-event massage
B = Pre-event massage
C = Rehabilitative massage
D = Restorative massage

_____ 1. focuses on the restoration of tissue function following injury

_____ 2. given within the first hour or two after participating in an event

_____ 3. breaks down transverse adhesions that may have resulted from previous injuries

_____ 4. warms and loosens the muscles causing hyperemia in specific muscle areas

_____ 5. can locate and relieve areas of stress that carry a high risk of injury

_____ 6. stimulates circulation and at the same time calms the nervous system

_____ 7. reduces fibrosis caused by muscle injury

_____ 8. given 15 to 45 minutes prior to an event

_____ 9. is considered a regular and valuable part of the athlete's training schedule

_____ 10. enables the athlete to reach his or her peak performance earlier in the event and maintain that performance longer

_____ 11. allows the athlete to train at a higher level of intensity, more consistently, with less chance of injury

_____ 12. three to four times as effective as rest in recovery from muscle fatigue

_____ 13. shortens the time it takes for an injury to heal

_____ 14. makes more intense and frequent workouts possible, thereby improving overall performance

_____ 15. prevents delayed onset of muscle soreness and reduces the time it takes for the body to recover from exertion

_____ 16. is fast paced and invigorating

_____ 17. accelerates healing so the athlete's "down time" is cut to a minimum

_____ 18. helps to form strong, pliable scar tissue

_____ 19. given after the athlete has had a chance to warm down from the exertion of the competition or exercise

True or False: If the following statements are true, write *true* in the space provided. If they are false, replace the italicized word with one that makes the statement true.

_____ 1. Pre-event massage increases flexibility and circulation and *replaces* the warm up before an event.

_____ 2. During *pre-event massage,* adhesions can be eliminated to reduce the chance of injury.

_____ 3. Post-event massage is given after competition and helps an athlete *cool down.*

_____ 4. *Post-event massage* is three to four times as effective as rest in recovery from muscle fatigue.

_____ 5. *Restorative massage* may resemble pre-event or post-event massage.

_____ 6. A *strain* involves the stretching or tearing of a ligament.

_____ 7. A grade I strain is the most severe.

_____ 8. As a muscle fiber contracts, the sarcolemma and the *endomysium* move as a unit.

Short Answer: Provide short answers to the following questions. Write your answers in the space provided.

1. What is the first step when giving a post-event massage?

   _____

2. After a long race, what are some conditions the therapist needs to watch for?

   _____

3. What action should the therapist take if strains, sprains, abrasions, or contusions are apparent?

   _____

4. When interviewing an athlete for determining a training massage program, what are five important questions to ask?

   a. _____

   b. _____

   c. _____

   d. _____

   e. _____

Completion: In the space provided, write the word or words that correctly completes each statement.

1. Athletic injuries that have a sudden and definite onset and are usually of relatively short duration are considered to be _____ injuries.

2. A muscle strain in which there is severe tearing and complete loss of function is called a grade _____ strain.

3. The therapist's indicator as to how intensely to work on an injury site is _____.

4. Athletic injuries that have a gradual onset, tend to last for a long time, or reoccur often are considered _____ injuries.

Short Answer: Provide short answers to the following questions. Write your answers in the space provided.

1. Give six examples of acute athletic injuries.

    a. _____   b. _____

    c. _____   d. _____

    e. _____   f. _____

2. What effect does RICE have on soft tissue injuries?

    _____

3. When can massage be started on injured tissue?

    _____

4. What are two goals the therapist strives to achieve when working on chronic conditions?

    a. _____

    b. _____

5. List two positive effects of the swelling that results from tissue damage.

    a. _____

    b. _____

6. List three negative effects of swelling that results from tissue damage.

    a. _____

    b. _____

    c. _____

147

Key Choices: Identify the following conditions as either chronic or acute. Write the appropriate letter next to the conditions described below.

        C = Chronic

        A = Acute

_____ 1. dislocated shoulder

_____ 2. iliotibial band syndrome

_____ 3. shin splints

_____ 4. broken wrist

_____ 5. overuse syndrome

_____ 6. torn ligament

_____ 7. sprained ankle

_____ 8. tennis elbow

_____ 9. bruised hip

_____ 10. tendonitis

Completion: In the space provided, write the word or words that correctly completes each statement.

1. The tensile strength of connective tissue is provided by _____.

2. The layer of connective tissue that closely covers an individual muscle is the _____.

3. Connective tissue extends beyond the end of the muscle to become _____.

4. The perimysium extends inward from the epimysium and separates the muscle into bundles of muscle fibers or _____.

5. Each muscle fiber is covered by a delicate connective tissue covering called the _____.

6. Soft tissue injuries result in the tearing of _____ in the connective tissue.

7. Collagen fibers are produced by _____.

8. Collagen formation that reconnects the injured tissue forms _____.

9. Collagen fibers that connect to structures other than the injured tissue form _____ that restrict mobility.

10. Proper _____ reduces the degree of secondary trauma following soft tissue injury.

CHAPTER 17

Specialized Massage

Completion: In the space provided, write the word or words that correctly completes each statement.

1. The massage practitioner can sharpen his or her skills and stay current to new developments in the massage field through _____.

2. Massage given to a pregnant woman is commonly called _____.

3. The main goal of prenatal massage is _____.

Short Answer: Provide short answers to the following questions. Write your answers in the space provided.

1. What are two considerations when positioning a pregnant woman for massage?

   a. _____

   b. _____

2. Why is the supine position not recommended during the later stages of pregnancy?

   _____

3. What is the major general contraindication for massage during pregnancy?

   _____

Completion: In the space provided, write the word or words that correctly completes each statement.

1. The Dane credited with developing manual lymph drainage massage was _____.

2. Thin-walled tubes that collect lymph from interstitial fluid in the tissues are called _____.

3. White blood cells produced in the lymph system are known as _____.

4. Small bean-shaped masses of lymphatic tissue located along the course of lymph vessels are termed _____.

5. The principal manipulations used in lymph massage are _____ and _____.

Short Answer: Provide short answers to the following questions. Write your answers in the space provided.

1. Where does lymph re-enter the blood stream?

   _____

2. What portion of the interstitial fluid that is reabsorbed into the circulatory system becomes lymph?

   _____

3. What causes lymph to move through the system?

   _____

   _____

4. The two main functions of lymph nodes are:

   a. _____

   b. _____

5. What kind of massage is applied to neurolymphatic reflexes?

   _____

6. In what direction is lymph massage given?

   _____

7. When doing lymph massage on the leg, where should the manipulations begin?

   _____

Completion: In the space provided, write the word or words that correctly completes each statement.

1. Massage styles that are directed toward the deeper tissue structures of the muscle and fascia are commonly called _____ massage.

2. Rolfing was developed by _____.

3. Neurophysiological therapies recognize the link between the _____ system and the _____ system.

4. Alterations or disturbances in the neuromuscular relationship often result in _____ and _____.

5. A hyperirritable spot that is painful when compressed is called a _____.

6. When a point is compressed and it refers pain to another area of the body, that point is considered a(n) _____.

7. If a point is hypersensitive when compressed but does not refer pain, it is considered a _____.

8. The technique used by massage therapists where direct pressure is applied to the trigger point is known as _____.

Short Answer: Provide short answers to the following questions. Write your answers in the space provided.

1. What are three types of neuro-physiological therapies?

    a. _____

    b. _____

    c. _____

2. Where are myofascial trigger points found?

    _____

3. What is the neurological phenomenon that links a trigger point to its associated dysfunctional tissue?

    _____

4. How are taut bands of muscle located?

    _____

5. What are three common areas associated with the muscle where trigger points are found?

    a. _____

    b. _____

    c. _____

6. List four common procedures for deactivating trigger points.

    a. _____

    b. _____

    c. _____

    d. _____

7. What is the regulating factor in determining how much pressure to use when deactivating trigger points?

    _____

8. When a trigger point has been released, what action should be taken on the muscle where it was located?

    _____

151

Short Answer: Provide short answers to the following questions. Write your answers in the space provided.

1. Who originally developed Neuromuscular Therapy in the 1930s?

   _____

2. What are common abnormal signs associated with neuromuscular lesions?

   a. _____

   b. _____

   c. _____

   d. _____

   e. _____

   f. _____

   g. _____

   h. _____

   i. _____

3. Besides trigger points, what other areas does Neuromuscular Therapy (NMT) recognize that may be tender when palpated?

   _____

4. The main massage manipulations used in NMT are:

   a. _____

   b. _____

   c. _____

   d. _____

Completion: In the space provided, write the word or words that correctly complete each statement.

1. A therapeutic procedure that is used to improve the functional mobility of the joints and goes by the acronym MET is _____.

2. The two basic inhibitory reflexes produced during MET manipulations are _____ _____ and _____.

Short Answer: Provide short answers to the following questions. Write your answers in the space provided.

1. The three main variations of MET are:

   a. _____

   b. _____

   c. _____

2. Which of the three variations of MET use post-isometric relaxation?

_____

3. Which of the three variations of MET use reciprocal inhibition?

_____

4. What conditions respond best to MET?

_____

Short Answer: Provide short answers to the following questions. Write your answers in the space provided.

1. The gentlest of soft tissue manipulations when addressing mobility restrictions due to pain and soft tissue dysfunction are _____.

2. Three bodywork systems that incorporate this technique are:

   a. _____

   b. _____

   c. _____

3. What is the difference between these three techniques?

   _____

4. Strain-counterstrain (tender point) technique was developed by _____.

5. What is the main treatment in strain-counterstrain?

   _____

   _____

   _____

6. Orthobionomy was developed by an English osteopath named _____.

7. The hands-on manipulations used in orthobionomy are _____ and _____.

8. The main physical techniques used in structural muscular balancing include:

   a. _____

   b. _____

   c. _____

   d. _____

9. What are the two main goals of structural muscular balancing?

    a. _____

    b. _____

Completion: In the space provided, write the word or words that correctly completes each statement.

1. A traditional Chinese medical practice whereby the skin is punctured with needles at specific points for therapeutic purposes is known as _____.

2. Religious philosophies of the Far East speak of _____ or "the way" or "that which is all there is."

3. In Eastern philosophies the opposing yet complementary aspects of existence are represented by _____ and _____.

Matching: Arrange the following words in two columns. In the first column, list words that correspond to *yin*. In the second column, write the words that correspond to *yang* adjacent to the contrasting word in the *yin* column.

active	back of the body	cold	contracting
dark	day	deficient	excessive
expanding	forceful	front of the body	high
hot	inner body	inside	light
low	lower body	night	outer body
outside	overactive	passive	underactive
upper body	weak		

YIN

_____

_____

_____

_____

_____

_____

_____

_____

_____

_____

_____

_____

YANG

_____

_____

_____

_____

_____

_____

_____

_____

_____

_____

_____

_____

Completion: In the space provided, write the word or words that correctly completes each statement.

1. The interaction of *yin* and *yang* creates a vibratory force or energy called _____.

2. In the human body, there are three sources of this vital force. They are:

   a. _____

   b. _____

   c. _____

3. According to ancient philosophy, this vital force manifests itself as five interrelated elements. They are:

   a. _____   d. _____

   b. _____   e. _____

   c. _____

4. *Chi* moves through the body in specific channels called _____.

5. There are _____ bilateral channels that relate to the organs.

6. Along these channels are small areas of high conductivity called

   _____.

7. A number of treatment systems that incorporate various manipulations (not needles) on acupoints are collectively called _____.

8. The Japanese system of finger pressure massage is called _____.

9. The art and science of stimulating certain points on the body (especially the hands and feet) that effect organs or functions in distant parts of the body is known as _____.

Therapeutic Exercise

Completion: In the space provided, write the word or words that correctly completes each statement.

1. Exercise that is done with the intent of improving some physical condition is considered

   _____.

2. The principle of applying stresses to the body greater than it is accustomed to in order to cause physiological change is known as the _____ principle.

3. The body changes to tolerate the increased load through the process of _____.

4. The ability of a muscle or muscle group to contract and produce tension with a force exerted on some resistance is called _____.

5. The strength of a muscle is measured by _____.

6. The increased bulk of a muscle and increased density of the capillary bed within the muscle is called

   _____.

7. The muscle fibers controlled by a single motor neuron are collectively called a _____.

8. In order for adaptive increases in strength to occur, the muscles must contract against a force that is at least _____ percent of the maximum capacity.

9. In order to increase muscle function, the muscle must be exercised to a point of _____.

10. Maximum resistance with low reps tends to build muscle _____ and _____.

11. Lighter resistance with high repetitions builds muscle _____.

Short Answer: Provide short answers to the following questions. Write your answers in the space provided.

1. Before suggesting an exercise to a client, what must the therapist know:

   a. about the exercise?

   _____

   b. about the client?

   _____

2. What is the goal of therapeutic exercise?

_____

3. List five physiological areas that can be improved through therapeutic exercise.

a. _____

b. _____

c. _____

d. _____

e. _____

4. List four factors that determine the relative strength of a muscle.

a. _____

b. _____

c. _____

d. _____

5. What is the main disadvantage of isometric strengthening exercises?

_____

6. List three possible sources of resistance for isotonic exercises.

a. _____

b. _____

c. _____

True or False: If the following statements are true, write *true* in the space provided. If they are false, replace the italicized word with one that makes the statement true.

_____ 1. The increased bulk of a muscle is the result of an increase in the thickness of the *actin and myosin filaments*.

_____ 2. The larger the cross-sectional size of the muscle, the greater the *endurance*.

_____ 3. Most *strengthening* exercises increase muscle strength and endurance.

_____ 4. A maximum isometric contraction will generate approximately 20 percent more force than a maximum *eccentric* contraction.

_____ 5. During isotonic exercises, eccentric contractions should be *slower* than concentric contractions for maximum benefit.

_____ 6. As a muscle contracts through its available range of motion, the *force* it generates varies.

Key Choices: Choose the types of muscle contractions that best fit the descriptions or are most likely to produce the following effects. Write the appropriate letter next to the stated description or effect in the space provided.

A. concentric contraction   C. isometric contraction
B. eccentric contraction   D. isotonic contraction

_____ 1. Movement occurs.

_____ 2. The muscle length remains the same.

_____ 3. The muscle lengthens during the contraction.

_____ 4. The force of the contraction is different than the resistance.

_____ 5. The force of the contraction is equal to the resistance.

_____ 6. The force of contraction is greater than the resistance.

_____ 7. There is no perceivable movement.

_____ 8. The muscle shortens during the contraction.

_____ 9. The force of the contraction is less than the resistance.

Completion: In the space provided, write the word or words that correctly completes each statement.

1. Exercises that provide a maximum load at several points during a muscle contraction are _____ exercises.

2. During manual resistance exercises, resistance is provided by _____ _____.

3. The direction of the resistance in manual resistance exercises is _____ _____.

4. The point of therapist contact in manual resistance exercises is _____ _____.

5. Body weight exercises use _____ to supply the resistance.

6. Push-ups and pull-ups are examples of _____ exercises.

7. The ability to carry on an activity over a prolonged period of time and resist fatigue is called _____.

8. Two body systems affected by endurance training are the _____ and _____ systems.

9. General endurance is sometimes called _____ endurance.

10. The ability of an individual to continue a general exercise over an extended period of time is called _____.

11. General endurance can be improved with regular _____.

12. The amount of stress or overload put on the cardiovascular system by aerobic exercise is related to the _____ of the exercise.

Short Answer: Provide short answers to the following questions. Write your answers in the space provided.

1. What are two advantages to body weight exercises?

   a. _____

   b. _____

2. List three examples of mechanical resistance equipment.

   a. _____

   b. _____

   c. _____

3. List four factors that determine the effectiveness of aerobic exercise.

   a. _____

   b. _____

   c. _____

   d. _____

4. Name four pieces of mechanical exercise equipment that are designed to improve cardiovascular fitness.

   a. _____

   b. _____

   c. _____

   d. _____

5. List at least seven aerobic activities.

   a. _____   e. _____

   b. _____   f. _____

   c. _____   g. _____

   d. _____

6. What is the recommended frequency for aerobic exercise to maintain cardiorespiratory fitness?

   _____

7. What is the formula for determining a person's maximum heart rate?

   _____

8. According to the American College of Sports Medicine, at what intensity are the optimum benefits of cardiovascular training obtained?

   _____

   _____

9. Determine the high and low heart rate limit for cardiopulmonary benefit for an individual thirty-two years of age.

   a. _____

   b. _____

10. List the three basic components of an aerobic workout.

   a. _____

   b. _____

   c. _____

11. List five physiological adaptations that result from regular aerobic exercise.

   a. _____

   b. _____

   c. _____

   d. _____

   e. _____

12. List six benefits of cardiorespiratory fitness.

   a. _____

   b. _____

   c. _____

   d. _____

   e. _____

   f. _____

13. List five factors that may result in reduced flexibility.

   a. _____

   b. _____

   c. _____

   d. _____

   e. _____

14. What are two physiological changes that take place that allow elongation of muscle tissue.

a. _____

b. _____

Completion: In the space provided, write the word or words that correctly completes each statement.

1. The ability of a joint to move freely and painlessly through its range of motion is called _____.

2. When decreased extensibility of muscle or other tissues crossing the joint causes reduced joint mobility, it is termed a _____.

3. The ability of tissue to return to normal resting length when stress is removed from it is called _____.

4. The property that allows tissues to change shape and adapt to ongoing stresses and conditions is termed _____.

5. Exercises that move the affected segment of the body through its available movement are called _____.

6. If the body segment is moved by some external force without the voluntary contractions of the muscles acting upon that segment, it is called _____.

7. The type of manipulation used to determine where limitations of movement exist but which does not challenge those limitations is called _____.

8. Range of motion done by an individual voluntarily contracting muscles is called _____ range of motion.

9. Elongating of soft tissue in order to maintain or increase full range of motion is accomplished with _____.

10. The sensory receptors responsible for the myotatic reflex are the _____ and the _____.

11. Sensory organs, located in the muscles, that monitor the velocity and extent of muscle movement are called _____.

12. Sensory organs, located near musculotendinous junctions, that monitor tension are the _____.

13. The myotatic reflex is initiated when _____ and causes _____.

14. _____ stretching moves a body segment beyond its free range of motion, while the muscles that act on that segment remain relaxed.

15. In _____ stretching, another person or therapist moves the client's body into the stretching positions, while the client remains relaxed.

16. Stretching techniques that utilize neuromuscular reflexes to enhance the elongation of muscles are referred to as _____ stretches.

17. When a muscle acting on a joint contracts and the muscle that causes the opposite action is reflexively inhibited, the physiological process is called _____.

18. The complex neuromuscular process of using the correct sequence of muscular movements with the right timing and force is referred to as _____.

19. Improving skill and coordination requires _____ and _____.

20. The relationship and alignment of body parts usually observed in the standing position is referred to as _____.

21. When the body is balanced between left and right, back and front, and the segments of the axial skeleton are properly aligned, a person is said to have _____.

True or False: If the following statements are true, write *true* in the space provided. If they are false, replace the italicized word with one that makes the statement true.

_____ 1. The *plastic* property of fibrous tissue regulates its flexibility.

_____ 2. Range of motion exercises are effective for *increasing* flexibility.

_____ 3. *Ballistic* stretches suppress the stretch reflex and inhibit the GTO.

_____ 4. The *Golgi tendon organs*, located in the muscle belly, sense the extent of muscle movement.

_____ 5. *Expiration* takes place because of the contraction of the diaphragm.

Short Answer: Provide short answers to the following questions. Write your answers in the space provided.

1. How much force is used in manual passive stretching exercises?

   _____

2. What four aspects of a manual passive stretch does the therapist control?

   a. _____

   b. _____

   c. _____

   d. _____

3. What are three variations of the reflexive inhibition stretching technique?

   a. _____

   b. _____

   c. _____

4. Name three sets of auxiliary muscles that assist during deep inhalation.

   a. _____

   b. _____

   c. _____

5. Why is it important to breathe through the nose instead of the mouth?

   _____

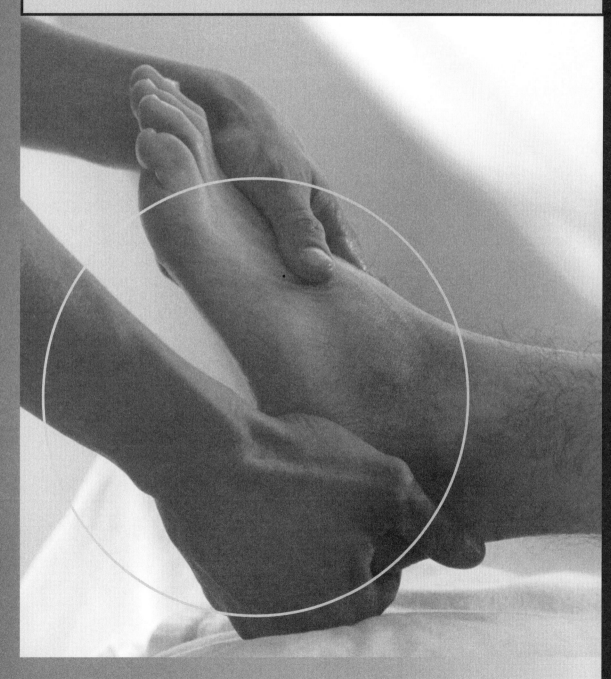

MASSAGE BUSINESS ADMINISTRATION

PART IV

Business Practices

Short Answer: Provide short answers to the following questions. Write your answers in the space provided.

1. When does business planning begin?

   _____

2. When does business planning end?

   _____

3. Name four important parts of business planning.

   a. _____

   b. _____

   c. _____

   d. _____

4. What are three common types of business operations?

   a. _____

   b. _____

   c. _____

Completion: In the space provided, write the word or words that correctly completes each statement.

1. A short general statement of the main focus of the business is called the _____.

2. Specific, attainable, measurable things or accomplishments that you set and make a commitment to achieve are termed _____.

3. If you are an individual owner of a business and carry all expenses, obligations, liabilities, and assets, you are considered a _____.

4. In order to establish a _____, a charter must be obtained from the state in which the business operates.

5. Management of a corporation is carried on by a _____.

6. When beginning a business, the expenses incurred before any revenues are collected are considered _____

7. Two primary reasons for the failure of small businesses are _____ and _____.

Short Answer: Provide short answers to the following questions. Write your answers in the space provided.

1. If your business is a sole proprietorship, who is responsible for any losses or debts?

_____

2. What zoning requirements must be considered when choosing a massage business location?

_____

3. List at least two important considerations when buying an established business.

a. _____

b. _____

c. _____

Completion: In the space provided, write the word or words that correctly completes each statement.

1. If a business is operating under a name other than the owner's, a _____ is required.

2. If the business sells products or if services are taxed, a _____ must be obtained from _____.

3. To assure the business meets zoning requirements, the _____ should be contacted.

4. An Employer Identification Number (EIN) must be obtained from the _____ if the business hires employees.

5. The identification number issued to licensed healthcare providers and used when submitting claims to medical insurance companies is called a _____.

6. As a massage business owner, one should have adequate insurance against _____, _____ , and _____.

Key Choices: Choose the types of insurance that best fits the description. Write the appropriate letter next to the stated description in the space provided.

A. automobile insurance   E. liability insurance
B. disability insurance   F. malpractice insurance
C. fire and theft insurance   G. workers' compensation insurance
D. health insurance

_____ 1. protects the individual from loss of income because they are unable to work due to long-term illness or injury

_____ 2. helps cover the cost of medical bills, especially hospitalization, serious injury, or illness

_____ 3. provides medical and liability insurance to the driver and any passengers

_____ 4. is required if you have employees

_____ 5. covers the cost of fixtures, furniture, equipment, products, and supplies

_____ 6. covers costs of injuries and litigation resulting from injuries sustained on the owner's property

_____ 7. covers the medical costs for the employee if they are injured on the job

_____ 8. covers the vehicle and its contents, regardless of who is at fault

_____ 9. protects the therapist from lawsuits filed by a client because of injury or loss that results from negligence or substandard performance

Completion: In the space provided, write the word or words that correctly completes each statement.

1. The standards of acceptable and professional behavior by which a person or business conducts business are called _____.

2. When setting your fees for massage, the _____ and the_____ should be considered.

3. A summary of all sales and cash receipts is called an _____.

4. A ledger that records, separates, and classifies business expenditures is called a _____.

Short Answer: Provide short answers to the following questions. Write your answers in the space provided.

1. If a massage business is operated out of a home, are all telephone expenses tax deductible?

    _____

2. For a self-employed massage practitioner, what three major records should be maintained?

    a. _____

    b. _____

    c. _____

3. Two important reasons for keeping accurate financial records are:

   a. _____

   b. _____

4. Why is it advisable to consult an accountant when preparing taxes?

   _____

   _____

5. What name is on the business checking account?

   _____

6. What moneys are deposited in the business account?

   _____

7. For what purposes are checks written from the business account?

   _____

8. What is the purpose of a petty cash fund?

   _____

9. Where does petty cash fund money come from?

   _____

10. How long should canceled checks and bank statements be kept for tax purposes?

    _____

11. What is included in the income records?

    _____

12. Name ten things that should be included on an income receipt or invoice.

    a. _____   f. _____

    b. _____   g. _____

    c. _____   h. _____

    d. _____   i. _____

    e. _____   j. _____

13. How many copies of the invoice should there be and where do they go?

    _____

14. Information that is included in each entry of the disbursement ledger includes:

    a. _____

    b. _____

    c. _____

    d. _____

    e. _____

15. What receipts should be kept and filed?

    _____

16. How long should receipts be kept?

    _____

17. When is it necessary to keep an accounts receivable file?

    _____

18. A record of money owed to other persons or businesses is kept in an _____ file.

19. Items and equipment purchased to be used in the business for an extended period of time (more than a year) are called _____.

20. Are the products that are for sale in the business considered business assets?

    _____

21. What information should be kept in a record of business assets?

    _____

    _____

22. What are two methods of determining business-related automobile expenses?

    _____

23. What is usually kept in a client record?

    a. _____

    b. _____

    c. _____

24. What is the importance of an appointment book?

    _____

    _____

Completion: In the space provided, write the word or words that correctly completes each statement.

1. The business activity done to promote and increase business is called _____.

2. A segment of the population with similar characteristics that the practitioner may prefer to attract is his or her _____.

3. Most promotional activities are _____ in nature.

4. Any marketing activity that the practitioner must pay for directly is considered _____.

5. The practice of encouraging clients to come back for services repeatedly is known as _____.

Short Answer: Provide short answers to the following questions. Write your answers in the space provided.

1. List five marketing activities.

   a. _____

   b. _____

   c. _____

   d. _____

   e. _____

2. What is the advantage of selecting a target market?

   _____

   _____

3. What are two ways of determining a target market?

   a. _____

   b. _____

4. What are two objectives of promotional activities?

   a. _____

   b. _____

5. Give three examples of promotional activities.

   a. _____

   b. _____

   c. _____

6. Give four examples of promotional materials.

    a. _____

    b. _____

    c _____

    d. _____

7. What should be included on every piece of promotional material?

    _____

8. List four ways to promote business through public relations.

    a. _____

    b. _____

    c. _____

    d. _____

9. What are two main sources for obtaining referrals?

    a. _____

    b. _____

10. When a satisfied client refers a new person, what should be done?

    _____

11. When a healthcare professional refers a client, what should be done?

    a. _____

    b. _____

    c. _____

12. What are the three "R's" of referrals?

    a. _____

    b. _____

    c. _____

Short Answer: Provide short answers to the following questions. Write your answers in the space provided.

1. What federal regulations must be observed when operating a massage business with employees?

   a. _____

   b. _____

   c. _____

2. What state regulations must be observed when operating a massage business?

   a. _____

   b. _____

   c. _____

   d. _____

   e. _____

Multiple Choice Questions

Directions: Carefully read each statement. Choose the word of phrase that correctly completes the meaning and write the corresponding letter in the blank provided.

Chapter 1
Historical Overview of Massage

1. The systematic manual or mechanical manipulation of the body's soft tissues is called _____
   a) shiatsu   c) physical therapy
   b) massage   d) chiropractic

2. In the past, a female massage person was usually called a _____
   a) madame   c) monsieur
   b) masseur   d) masseuse

3. Increased circulation, muscle relaxation, and pain relief are _____
   a) problems of massage   c) medical conditions
   b) benefits of massage   d) massage movements

4. Massage has been part of Western medical traditions for at least _____
   a) 10 years   c) 3000 years
   b) 200 years   d) 10,000 years

5. Modern Chinese massage is called _____
   a) amna   c) chi gong
   b) shiatsu   d) tuina

6. The use of the term massage to denote the practice of manipulating the soft tissues first appeared in American or European literature around _____
   a) 1875   c) 1774
   b) 1925   d) 1850

7. A finger pressure technique used by the Japanese is called
   a) shiatsu   c) tsubo
   b) tuina   d) acupuncture

_____

8. The popularity of bathing and massage lessened with the
   a) decline of the Roman Empire   c) invention of electricity
   b) invention of hot tubs   d) Inquisition

_____

9. Much of Greco-Roman culture was preserved by the
   a) Spanish   c) Turks
   b) Romans   d) Persians

_____

10. The father of physical therapy is
   a) Taylor   c) Aesculapius
   b) Hippocrates   d) Per Henrik Ling

_____

11. In the Swedish Movement System, movements are classified as active, duplicated, and
   a) passive   c) gliding
   b) repetitive   d) restrictive

_____

12. The Swedish Movement Cure was brought to the United States by
   a) Douglas Graham   c) the Taylor brothers
   b) Ambroise Pare   d) Dr. Johann Mezger

_____

13. The Greek physician/priest credited with founding the first gymnasiums in the seventh century BC was
   a) Homer   c) Herodicus
   b) Hippocrates   d) Aesculapius

_____

14. Much of modern massage terminology is based on terms from this language:
   a) Italian   c) Greek
   b) Chinese   d) French

_____

15. Public interest in massage reemerged in the United States around
   a) 1950   c) l960
   b) 1970   d) 1980

_____

16. National certification in massage and bodywork has been available in the United States since
   a) 1961   c) l985
   b) 1972   d) 1992

_____

17. The finger pressure massage method called shiatsu is
   a) Japanese   c) German
   b) Chinese   d) French

_____

18. The Trager® method uses movement exercises called
   a) gymnastics   c) aerobics
   b) mentastics   d) athletics

19. Aligning major body segments through manipulation of connective tissue is _____
    a) the Rolfing® method
    c) the Palmer method
    b) the Trager® method
    d) reflexology

20. The idea that stimulation of particular body points affects other areas is called _____
    a) chiropractic
    c) Rolfing®
    b) reflexology
    d) Trager®

Chapter 2
Requirements for the Practice of Therapeutic Massage

1. *Scope of practice* defines   _____
   a) legally acceptable professional   c) specific techniques
      activities
   b) medical ethics   d) geographical boundaries

2. If a client's condition is outside the massage technician's scope of practice,
   the technician should   _____
   a) schedule extra sessions   c) take more training
   b) refer the client to the proper   d) refer to textbooks
      professional

3. The main reason for massage licensing is   _____
   a) to make sure only people who   c) to protect the health, safety,
      graduate from special schools   and welfare of the public
      practice
   b) to insure that only certain kinds   d) to close down massage parlors
      of massage are practiced

4. Testing and licensing of massage professionals is generally overseen by   _____
   a) a regulatory board   c) a professional massage association
   b) the legislature   d) a local law enforcement agency

5. Being licensed in one city or state _____ validation in another location.   _____
   a) does not guarantee   c) guarantees
   b) requires   d) assumes

6. The education standard recommended by the National Certification for
   Therapeutic Massage and Bodywork is   _____
   a) 300 hours   c) 1000 hours
   b) 150 hours   d) 500 hours

7. A document awarded in recognition of achieving or maintaining a set standard
   is a/an   _____
   a) recommendation   c) certificate
   b) license   d) diploma

8. Completing a course of study or passing an exam results in   _____
   a) certification   c) a diploma
   b) licensing   d) job security

9. Certificates can be awarded by   _____
   a) schools   c) institutions
   b) professional organizations   d) all the above

Chapter 3
Professional Ethics for Massage Practitioners

1. The code of morals of a profession, group, or individual is called ⎯⎯⎯⎯
   a) values
   b) attitudes
   c) morals
   d) ethics

2. An individual in an occupation that requires advanced training to gain skills and knowledge is considered a ⎯⎯⎯⎯
   a) journeyman
   b) professional
   c) skilled laborer
   d) veteran

3. A massage therapist's best method of advertising is ⎯⎯⎯⎯
   a) satisfied clients
   b) newspaper
   c) radio
   d) television

4. Intimate or sexual relationships between client and practitioner are ⎯⎯⎯⎯
   a) avoided
   b) done only with full consent
   c) not done in the massage facility
   d) done only for therapeutic reasons

5. Keep your knowledge current by ⎯⎯⎯⎯
   a) attending seminars
   b) reading trade journals
   c) joining professional associations
   d) doing all the above

1. The scientific study of body movement is
   a) anatomy
   b) kinesiology
   c) pathology
   d) physiology
   _____

2. Normal functions of bodily systems are studied in
   a) physiology
   b) histology
   c) anatomy
   d) pathology
   _____

3. The study of the gross structure of the body or an organism and its parts is known as
   a) physiology
   b) histology
   c) anatomy
   d) pathology
   _____

4. Describing how the organs or body parts function and relate to one another is
   a) physiology
   b) histology
   c) anatomy
   d) pathology
   _____

5. The branch of biology concerned with the microscopic structure of living tissues is
   a) physiology
   b) histology
   c) anatomy
   d) pathology
   _____

6. The study of structural and functional changes caused by disease is
   a) physiology
   b) histology
   c) anatomy
   d) pathology
   _____

7. Lower blood pressure and general relaxation are _____ effects of massage.
   a) recurring
   b) indirect
   c) direct
   d) reflex
   _____

8. The body's internal balance is called
   a) blood chemistry
   b) breathing
   c) homeostasis
   d) physiology
   _____

9. Perceived conditions such as dizziness, nausea, or pain are called
   a) symptoms
   b) diseases
   c) homeostasis
   d) signs
   _____

10. Observable indications such as fever, abnormal pulse rate, or abnormal skin color are
    a) symptoms of disease
    b) illnesses
    c) signs of disease
    d) psychosomatic
    _____

11. Any psychological or physical situation or condition that causes tension or strain is called
    a) disease
    b) stress
    c) pathology
    d) trauma
    _____

12. The adrenal hormone that acts as an anti-inflammatory and anti-allergenic in stressful situations is
   a) DMSO
   b) cortisol
   c) estrogen
   d) adrenaline

13. A condition that responds well to massage and is associated with muscle spasms and ischemic pain is
   a) hyperthermia
   b) the myotatic reflex
   c) the pain-spasm-pain cycle
   d) a low back herniated disc

14. Prolonged adrenal excretions make the body
   a) exhausted
   b) energetic
   c) strong
   d) ecstatic

15. The pain-spasm-pain cycle is associated with
   a) headaches
   b) heart attacks
   c) muscle spasms
   d) mental health

16. The condition in which contracted muscles inhibit blood flow to an area is called _____
   a) constriction
   b) ischemia
   c) hypertension
   d) bruising

17. When tissue is damaged, _____ migrate to the area to engulf and digest invading organisms and tissue debris.
   a) free nerve endings
   b) red blood cells
   c) fibroblasts
   d) leukocytes

18. The existence of disease-producing organisms throughout the body is termed a/an
   a) microorganism
   b) inflammation
   c) systemic infection
   d) local infection

19. A protective tissue response characterized by swelling, redness, heat, and pain is _____
   a) ischemia
   b) spasm
   c) sun burn
   d) inflammation

20. When injured by trauma or infection, neurons of the central nervous system
   a) repair slowly
   b) don't repair
   c) require transplants
   d) heal quickly

21. In medical terminology, the root word usually indicates the
   a) number
   b) body part
   c) condition
   d) treatment

22. The medical term prefix "a" means
   a) one
   b) many
   c) without
   d) after

23. The medical term prefix "ambi" means
   a) in twos
   b) both
   c) walking
   d) movement

24. The medical-term prefix "infra" means
   a) beneath
   b) above
   c) inside
   d) outside

25. The medical-term suffix "algia" means
   a) three
   b) binding
   c) inflammation
   d) painful condition

26. The medical-term suffix "itis" means
   a) inflammation
   b) old
   c) resembling
   d) tumor

27. The medical term suffix "pathic" means
   a) germs
   b) tumor
   c) toxic
   d) diseased

28. The medical term root "arth(ro)" means
   a) joint
   b) bone
   c) blood
   d) lung

29. The medical term root "derm" means
   a) teeth
   b) bone
   c) skin
   d) lung

1. All substances are made from subatomic particles that form
   a) molecules
   b) tissues
   c) atoms
   d) cells

2. The basic structure in human organisms is the
   a) organ
   b) tissue
   c) cell
   d) molecule

3. Cell division, which produces new cells, is called
   a) mutation
   b) mitosis
   c) amitosis
   d) gestation

4. The complex chemical and physical process that nourishes organisms is called
   a) mitosis
   b) metabolism
   c) homeostasis
   d) nutrition

5. Microscopic structures in the cytoplasm of the cell that produce energy needed for cellular work are called
   a) lysosomes
   b) mitochondria
   c) Golgi bodies
   d) endoplasmic reticulum

6. Anabolism and catabolism are closely regulated to maintain
   a) prophase
   b) enzymes
   c) amitosis
   d) homeostasis

7. Which of the following is not one of the five main human tissue types?
   a) epithelial
   b) connective
   c) nervous
   d) skeletal

8. A special molecule that stores energy for use in muscular activity is
   a) adenosine triphosphate
   b) fatty acids
   c) glucose
   d) protein

9. Bone, adipose tissue, epimysium and hyaline cartilage are
   a) areas of fat storage
   b) kinds of connective tissue
   c) skeletal structures
   d) common sites of inflammation

10. The thin tissue layer that forms the skin, organ coverings, and inner lining of all the hollow organs is the
    a) epithelial tissue
    b) connective tissue
    c) muscular tissue
    d) skin

11. Fibrous tissue between muscle bundles is called
    a) cartilage
    b) fascia
    c) muscular tissue
    d) perichondrium

12. The _____ membrane lines the inner joint cavities. _____
    a) synovial   c) mucous
    b) adipose   d) serous

13. The bands that attach muscles to bone are _____
    a) tendons   c) cartilage
    b) ligaments   d) aponeurosa

14. The tough, fibrous bands that connect bones to bones are _____
    a) tendons.   c) cartilage
    b) ligaments   d) fascia

15. Skeletal muscles are also known as _____
    a) voluntary muscles   c) tendonous muscles
    b) nonstriated muscles   d) smooth muscle

16. Cardiac muscle tissue occurs only in the _____
    a) liver   c) heart
    b) blood vessels   d) skeletal muscles

17. The imaginary line that divides the body into front and back halves is the _____
    a) coronal plane   c) midsagittal plane
    b) sagittal plane   d) transverse plane

18. The liver and stomach are contained in the _____
    a) dorsal cavity   c) abdominal cavity
    b) pelvic cavity   d) cranial cavity

19. The elbow is _____ to the wrist _____
    a) proximal   c) lateral
    b) medial   d) distal

20. The ribs are lateral to the _____
    a) arms   c) pelvis
    b) scapula   d) sternum

21. Lumbar refers to the region of the _____
    a) temple   c) lower back
    b) skull   d) pelvis

22. The epigastric area is _____
    a) the location of the bladder   c) the region of the tongue
    b) inferior to the diaphragm   d) anterior to the scapula

23. The human body has _____ important organ systems. _____
    a) 2   c) 10
    b) 5   d) 20

24. The largest organ of the body is the _____
    a) muscular system   c) liver
    b) skin   d) stomach

25. Protection, heat regulation, secretion, excretion, and absorption are functions of _____
    a) endocrine system
    c) muscles
    b) skin
    d) brain

26. Exposure to ultraviolet light causes the skin to darken by stimulating the production of _____
    a) melanin
    c) fibroblasts
    b) carotene
    d) hemoglobin

27. Collagen, reticulum, and elastin are the fibers in the cells of the _____
    a) epidermis
    c) dermis
    b) lymph
    d) blood

28. The skin gets its strength, form, and flexibility from _____
    a) collagenc)
    the muscles
    b) elastin
    d) subcutaneous tissue

29. A small discolored spot on the skin is a _____
    a) macule
    c) tumor
    b) bulla
    d) vesicle

30. An elevation of the skin having an inflamed base and containing pus is a _____
    a) papule
    c) pustule
    b) pimple
    d) wheal

31. A crack in the skin penetrating into the derma is called a _____
    a) fissure
    c) scab
    b) crust
    d) cut

32. Skin disorders are an area massage therapists should be able to _____
    a) treat successfully
    c) recognize and refer
    b) use vibration on
    d) apply antibiotic creams to

33. A generalized term for a structural change in tissue due to disease or injury is _____
    a) fracture
    c) hematoma
    b) lesion
    d) laceration

34. Flat bones are found in the _____
    a) knee
    c) leg
    b) skull
    d) spine

35. The number of bones in the human adult skeleton is _____
    a) 101
    c) 310
    b) 206
    d) 502

36. The bones of the upper and lower extremities form the _____
    a) axial skeleton
    c) skull
    b) spine
    d) appendicular skeleton

37. White blood cells are produced by the _____
    a) yellow bone marrow   c) osteoclasts
    b) lymphocytes   d) red bone marrow

38. A fracture in the shaft of the bone would be a break in the _____
    a) epiphysis   c) diaphysis
    b) epiphyseal plate   d) articular cartilage

39. Muscle tendon fibers attach to bone by interlacing with _____
    a) compact bone   c) periosteum
    b) ligaments   d) endosteum

40. Which of following is NOT a bone of the cranium? _____
    a) temporal   c) zygomatic
    b) sphenoid   d) parietal

41. The coracoid process is located _____
    a) on the scapula   c) on the pelvis
    b) behind the ear   d) at the proximal end of the ulna

42. Immovable joints are called _____
    a) ampiarthrotic   c) synarthrotic
    b) articulations   d) synovial

43. The range of motion of amphiarthrotic joints is _____
    a) 360 degrees   c) freely moving
    b) limited   d) in a single plane

44. An example of a diarthrotic joint is _____
    a) hip   c) intervertebral
    b) skull   d) the teeth

45. Greatest range of movement is from _____
    a) pivot joints   c) ball and socket joints
    b) hinge joints   d) saddle joints

46. A stretched ligament with some discomfort and minimal loss of function is a _____
    a) Class I strain   c) Class I sprain
    b) Class II sprain   d) Class III sprain

47. The ability of muscle to return to its original shape after being stretched is called _____
    a) contractility   c) elasticity
    b) resizing   d) shortening

48. The layer of connective tissue that covers an individual muscle is called _____
    a) fascicle   c) periosteum
    b) epimysium   d) endomysium

49. Each muscle fiber within a fascicle is covered by tissue called _____
    a) epimysium   c) endomysium
    b) periosteum   d) perimysium

50. Muscle's contractile ability is a result of the interaction between two filaments, myosin and
    a) actin
    b) elastin
    c) adenosine
    d) reticulin

51. What type of muscle tissue is found in the heart wall?
    a) non-striated
    b) cardiac
    c) smooth
    d) skeletal

52. The cell membrane of a muscle fiber is called the
    a) endomysium
    b) sarcolemma
    c) sarcoplasmic reticulum
    d) fascia

53. The striated appearance of skeletal muscles results from the
    a) sarcoplasmic reticulum network
    b) transverse tubule pattern
    c) sarcomere arrangement
    d) aerobic conversion

54. The strength of a muscle contraction is varied by changing the
    a) number of motor units stimulated
    b) strength that each individual fiber contracts
    c) number of fibers contracting within each motor unit
    d) the intensity of the nerve impulse

55. The transmission of the stimulus of muscle contraction is aided by
    a) myosin
    b) actin
    c) brain waves
    d) transverse tubules

56. Energy for muscle contractions comes from
    a) ATF
    b) CPA
    c) ADP
    d) ATP

57. _____ is found in the gap between the end of the motor nerve and the muscle fiber.
    a) Mitochondria
    b) Adenosine triphosphate
    c) Acetylcholine
    d) Creatine phosphate

58. The condition in which muscles cease to respond due to lack of oxygen and/or buildup of waste products is called
    a) muscle fatigue
    b) oxygen deficiency
    c) lactic acid
    d) anaerobic respiration

59. A muscle contraction in which the body part affected by the muscle does not move is called
    a) isotonic
    b) isometric
    c) eccentric
    d) concentric

60. A muscle contraction in which the distance between the ends of the muscle changes is called
    a) isotonic
    b) resistant
    c) dynamic
    d) isometric

61. The muscle that originates on the coracoid process and flexes the elbow is the _____
    a) brachioradialis   c) biceps brachii
    b) brachialis   d) coracobrachialis

62. A muscle that flexes the neck or turns the head to the opposite side is the _____
    a) splenius capitus   c) sternocleidomastoid
    b) scalenus posterior   d) all of the above

63. A muscle strain that involves a partial tear of 10% to 50% of the muscle fibers
    is classified _____
    a) Grade I   c) Grade III
    b) Grade II   d) parietal

64. A group of related genetic diseases that cause progressive degeneration of the
    voluntary muscular system is called _____
    a) muscular dystrophy   c) fibrosis
    b) myofibrosis   d) atrophy

65. Supplying the body with nutrients and carrying away waste products is the
    function of the _____
    a) lungs   c) kidneys
    b) circulatory system   d) muscles

66. The two-way diffusion of substances between the blood and tissue fluids
    surrounding cells is the function of the _____
    a) arteries   c) capillaries
    b) veins   d) lymph

67. Waste-laden blood returns to the heart through the _____
    a) veins   c) capillaries
    b) arteries   d) lymphatics

68. Blood platelets are important to proper _____
    a) nutrition   c) immunity
    b) clotting   d) circulation

69. Macrophages are large cells (WBc) that destroy foreign bacteria by the
    process of _____
    a) osmosis   c) phagocytosis
    b) mitosis   d) enzymatic action

70. The process in which substances move from an area of higher concentration to
    an area of lower concentration is _____
    a) diffusion   c) filtration
    b) osmosis   d) saturation

71. Blood is supplied to the small finger side of the hand by the _____
    a) ulnar artery   c) parietal artery
    b) popliteal artery   d) radial artery

72. The right atrium receives blood directly from _____
    a) the superior and inferior vena cava   c) the pulmonary veins
    b) the right ventricle   d) the coronary vein

73. The liquid that surrounds tissue cells is called
    a) lymph
    b) interstitial fluid
    c) plasma
    d) blood

74. Toxic molecules are filtered by the
    a) lymphatic system
    b) spleen
    c) muscular system
    d) bone marrow

75. Lymph re-enters the blood vascular system through the
    a) lymph capillaries
    b) lymph nodes
    c) spleen
    d) subclavian vein

76. Approximately how much of the fluid that leaves the blood vascular system is absorbed by the lymph-vascular system?
    a) 5%
    b) 10%
    c) 20%
    d) 40%

77. A condition in which there is an inadequate population of erythrocytes is
    a) hemophilia
    b) anemia
    c) edema
    d) leukemia

78. The junction at which impulses are passed from one neuron to another is called a/an
    a) axon
    b) neuromuscular junction
    c) synapse
    d) dendrite

79. The central nervous system consists of the spinal cord and the
    a) motor neurons
    b) afferent nerves
    c) mixed nerves
    d) brain

80. A motor neuron is also call a/an
    a) efferent neuron
    b) interneuron
    c) nerve cell
    d) afferent neuron

81. The three types of neurons are
    a) sympathetic, parasympathetic, peripheral
    b) afferent, efferent, connecting
    c) sensory, motor, interneuron
    d) receptors, affectors, conductors

82. Body balance and voluntary muscle movement are controlled by the
    a) cerebellum
    b) cerebrum
    c) brainstem
    d) midbrain

83. The spinal cord has _____ pairs of spinal nerves:
    a) 25
    b) 31
    c) 42
    d) 36

84. Movement of head, neck, and shoulders is controlled by the
    a) cervical plexus
    b) somatic system
    c) brachial plexus
    d) cranial nerves

85. All thought, association, and judgment take place in the _____
   a) cerebellum   c) cerebral cortex
   b) thalamus   d) medulla oblongata

86. The largest and longest nerve in the body is the _____ nerve.
   a) brachial   c) lumbar
   b) vagus   d) sciatic

87. Damage to the _____ nerve could cause inability of the diaphragm to function _____
   a) phrenic   c) hypoglossal
   b) axillary   d) pneumogastric

88. Nerves from the 5th, 6th, and 7th cervical vertebrae form the _____
   a) radial nerve   c) brachial plexus
   b) cervical plexus   d) ulnar nerve

89. Specialized nerve endings that sense the amount of tension produced in muscle
    cells are called   _____
   a) spindle cells   c) exteroceptors
   b) Golgi tendon organs   d) Ruffini nerve ends

90. Which of the following is considered peripheral nerves?   _____
   a) cranial nerves   c) sympathetic nerves
   b) spinal nerves   d) all of the above

91. The parasympathetic and sympathetic nervous systems constitute the   _____
   a) central nervous system   c) autonomic nervous system
   b) peripheral nervous system   d) none of the above

92. Various skin and intestinal glands belong to the   _____
   a) endocrine group   c) dermis
   b) exocrine group   d) digestive system

93. Glands that depend on blood and lymph to carry their secretions belong to the   _____
   a) endocrine group   c) neuron group
   b) exocrine group   d) messenger group

94. Insulin causes   _____
   a) a decrease in the level of blood   c) a decrease in the permeability of
      glucose   cell membranes to glucose
   b) an increase in the production of   d) none of the preceding
      glucose from glycogen

95. Endocrine glands secrete chemicals called   _____
   a) lymph   c) hormones
   b) neurotransmitters   d) enzymes

96. The gland that has both exocrine and endocrine qualities is the   _____
   a) thyroid   c) adrenal gland
   b) pancreas   d) kidney

97. The body's metabolism is regulated by the _____ gland. _____
    a) thyroid
    c) thymus
    b) pituitary
    d) adrenal

98. The hormone that represses or resolves conditions of inflammation is _____
    a) estrogen
    c) adrenaline
    b) thyroxin
    d) cortisol

99. Exchange of carbon dioxide and oxygen is called _____
    a) respiration
    c) oxidation
    b) relaxation
    d) ventilation

100. Internal respiration occurs between the blood and the _____
    a) cells
    c) lymph
    b) air
    d) lungs

101. Oxygen is carried from the lungs to body cells by linking (chemically bonding)
    with _____
    a) carbaminohemoglobin
    c) hemoglobin
    b) hydrogen ions
    d) carbonic acid

102. Normal adult respiration occurs this many times per minute: _____
    a) 10 to 15
    c) 14 to 20
    b) 25 to 30
    d) 40 to 50

103. The alimentary canal includes (not counting any accessory organs) _____
    a) mouth, teeth, throat, stomach
       and large intestines
    c) mouth, pharynx, esophagus,
       stomach, small and large intestines
    b) mouth, throat, pancreas, gall
       bladder and large intestines
    d) mouth, pharynx, pancreas,
       vermiform appendix, small and
       large intestine

104. Transfer of nutrients from the intestines to the blood or lymph is called _____
    a) absorption
    c) nutrition
    b) digestion
    d) osmosis

105. Metabolism is a series of chemical reactions that take place in the tissue cells.
    These reactions are necessary for _____
    a) building tissue and storing fat
    c) providing for elimination of
       waste products
    b) using nutritive elements to
       provide energy
    d) building and repairing tissue and
       releasing heat and energy

106. The small intestine consists of three parts, which, beginning at the stomach,
    appear in the following order: _____
    a) ileum, duodenum, jejunum
    c) jejunum, ileum, duodenum
    b) duodenum, jejunum, ileum
    d) duodenum, ileum, jejunum

107. Urine is produced in and eliminated from the organs of the urinary system in
    the following order:
    a) cortex, urethra, bladder, ureter
    c) kidney, pelvis, ureter, bladder
    b) kidney, urethra, bladder, ureter
    d) kidney, ureter, bladder, urethra

191

1. Indirect responses to touch that affect body functions are called
   a) reflex effects
   b) pressure points
   c) physical effects
   d) mechanical effects
   _____

2. Adhesion development and excessive scarring following trauma can be prevented or reduced with
   a) gliding movements
   b) petrissage
   c) friction massage
   d) percussion movements
   _____

3. In Swedish massage, movements should generally be
   a) toward the heart
   b) down the leg
   c) away from the heart
   d) invigorating
   _____

4. The term that means that the expected treatment is not advisable is
   a) indicators
   b) contraindicated
   c) incorrect
   d) inadmissible
   _____

5. A massage technique that increases the permeability of the capillary beds and produces an increased flow of interstitial fluid is
   a) active joint movements
   b) friction
   c) light stroking
   d) vibration
   _____

6. A contraindication of massage is
   a) mild high blood pressure
   b) AIDS
   c) muscle spasm
   d) fever
   _____

7. Acute inflammation is a massage
   a) side effect
   b) contraindication
   c) indication
   d) benefit
   _____

8. Inflammation of a vein is called
   a) thrombosis
   b) phlebitis
   c) embolism
   d) aneurosa
   _____

9. If a client comes for a massage and has a low-grade fever (100.5°F) the practitioner should
   a) have them drink plenty of water before and after the massage
   b) give them a very light massage
   c) refer them to a doctor
   d) make them an appointment for another time and send them home
   _____

10. A piece of a blood clot floating in the blood is called
    a) varicose
    b) phlebitis
    c) embolus
    d) aneurosa
    _____

11. A mass of blood trapped in tissue or a body cavity as a result of internal bleeding is called
    a) hematoma
    b) phlebitis
    c) contusion
    d) edema
    _____

12. Massage is contraindicated if edema is due to a
    a) headache
    b) hematoma
    c) protein imbalance
    d) varicosity

13. Cancer is a disease that is often spread through the
    a) genes
    b) lymphatic system
    c) blood
    d) digestive system

14. The method in which the client's arm is moved through its range of motion by the therapist while the client remains relaxed is
    a) passive joint movement
    b) active joint movement
    c) assisted joint movement
    d) contraindicated in muscle injuries

15. Any massage that increases lymph flow should not be performed on clients with
    a) mild edema
    b) joint problems
    c) cancer
    d) high blood pressure

16. Massage during pregnancy is
    a) contraindicated
    b) usually beneficial
    c) only done with a doctors approval
    d) avoided except under special conditions

17. The purpose of massage for the critically ill is to bring
    a) pleasure
    b) relaxation
    c) comfort
    d) all of the above

18. Body areas where caution should be used to avoid damaging underlying anatomical structures are called
    a) contraindications
    b) endangerment sites
    c) untouchable
    d) landmarks

1. The size of a massage room should be at least   _____
   a) 5 feet by 6 feet   c) 5 feet by 9 feet
   b) 10 feet by 12 feet   d) 15 feet by 20 feet

2. The ideal Fahrenheit temperature for a massage room is   _____
   a) 75 degrees   c) 80 degrees
   b) 65 degrees   d) 85 degrees

3. Matching massage movements to the tempo of the music is   _____
   a) desirable   c) not desirable
   b) unprofessional   d) professional

4. The height of a massage table is determined by the   _____
   a) height of the client   c) practitioner's height
   b) weight of the client   d) size of the room

5. The best covering for a massage table is   _____
   a) velvet   c) vinyl
   b) suede   d) cotton

6. If oil has an unpleasant odor but is not rancid, add a few drops of   _____
   a) lemon juice   c) vinegar
   b) essential oil   d) Lysol®

7. Cleansers, toners or astringents, and moisturizers are some of the products needed for   _____
   a) oily backs   c) hand massage
   b) facial massage   d) foot massage

8. The time to determine product allergies is   _____
   a) during consultation   c) at the end of massage
   b) at the beginning of massage d) during the second visit

Chapter 8
Sanitary and Safety Practices

1. Every state protects the public health through _____
   a) commissions   c) sanitation
   b) laws   d) inspections

2. Disease-producing bacteria are termed _____
   a) non-pathogenic   c) viruses
   b) pathogenic   d) antibodies

3. The mode of decontamination that destroys microorganisms including bacterial spores is _____
   a) antiseptics   c) disinfecting
   b) sanitation   d) sterilization

4. The practitioner's hands should be washed prior to client contact using _____
   a) disinfectant   c) alcohol
   b) antibacterial soap   d) detergent

5. One of the body's most important defenses against the invasion of harmful bacteria is _____
   a) healthy skin   c) clean hands
   b) good teeth   d) drinking liquids

6. A sign that the body is working to destroy harmful microorganisms is _____
   a) infection   c) immunity
   b) fluid retention   d) inflammation

7. What level of decontamination will be achieved by immersing implements in a 10% bleach solution for ten minutes? _____
   a) no decontamination will take place   c) disinfecting
   b) sanitizing   d) sterilizing

8. To disinfect linens, add to wash water l/4 to 1/2 cup of _____
   a) chlorine bleach   c) detergent
   b) ammonia   d) Lysol

9. Hands can be sanitized with _____
   a) quats   c) disinfectant
   b) soap and water   d) bleach

10. Sheets and towels with a rancid odor should be _____
   a) discarded   c) softened
   b) bleached   d) washed

11. Marking exits and having working fire extinguishers are two examples of _____
   a) housekeeping   c) fire safety
   b) equipment safety   d) first aid

12. Using proper lifting techniques when moving equipment or clients is an example of _____
    a) first aid
    b) product liability
    c) equipment safety
    d) personal safety

13. When going on an outcall, you should always _____
    a) bring extra towels
    b) tell someone your destination
    c) wear warm clothes
    d) drive yourself

1. The process of clarifying the appropriateness of an appointment is called _____
   - a) consultations
   - b) screening
   - c) selecting
   - d) discrimination.

2. Client information can be obtained by _____
   - a) consulting with a doctor
   - b) personal history forms
   - c) client interviews
   - d) all of the above

3. A thorough preliminary client assessment will include _____
   - a) client history
   - b) client observation
   - c) client examination
   - d) all the above

4. Noticing how the client holds his or her body and how he or she moves is called _____
   - a) body mechanics
   - b) observation
   - c) personology
   - d) subjective assessment

5. An outline that the practitioner can follow for giving treatments is called a/an _____
   - a) treatment plan
   - b) client history
   - c) recipe
   - d) client file

6. Work performed on a client is documented in the _____
   - a) treatment plan
   - b) client history
   - c) SOAP notes
   - d) billing records

7. Accurate records of a client's treatment help the therapist _____
   - a) achieve better results
   - b) abide by state laws
   - c) compare progress with other clients
   - d) charge higher fees

8. All client information should be considered _____
   - a) before calling their physician
   - b) research material
   - c) when diagnosing their condition
   - d) confidential

9. Normal human body temperature in degrees Fahrenheit is _____
   - a) 97.3
   - b) 98.6
   - c) 99.2
   - d) 101.1

10. Thermometers should be disinfected using _____
    - a) household disinfectant
    - b) bleach
    - c) alcohol
    - d) boiling water

1. Most current massage styles are based on
   a) Swedish movements   c) German movements
   b) Swiss movements   d) Chinese movements   _____

2. When a practitioner recognizes the purposes and effects of movements and
   adapts the treatment to the client, the massage practice has become   _____
   a) manipulative   c) therapeutic
   b) scientific   d) resourceful

3. Light movements are applied to bony parts or   _____
   a) muscles   c) vertebrae
   b) tendons   d) thin tissues

4. In Swedish massage, most manipulations are directed toward the   _____
   a) spine   c) feet
   b) heart   d) head

5. A massage practitioner's main mode of communication   _____
   a) is touch   c) is conversation during the treatment
   b) is during the consultation d) takes place after the session

6. A massage movement directed away from the heart is called   _____
   a) clockwise   c) contraindicated
   b) centripetal   d) centrifugal

7. A full-body massage can usually be completed in   _____
   a) half an hour   c) one hour
   b) two hours   d) one and one half hours

8. In massage, placing your hand, finger, or forearm on the client without movement is called   _____
   a) touch   c) intrusive
   b) gliding   d) friction

9. Sliding the hand over some portion of the client's body with varying amounts of
   pressure is called   _____
   a) friction   c) gliding
   b) kneading   d) vibration

10. Rapidly striking the hands against the surface of the client's body is called   _____
    a) percussion   c) petrissage
    b) friction   d) joint movement

11. When calming, stimulating, or anesthetizing effects are desired, the practitioner
    should use   _____
    a) friction   c) deep touch
    b) percussion   d) vibration

12. A type of gliding wherein the practitioner's hands glide the length of the client's entire body or body part without actually touching is called _____
    a) gliding
    b) aura stroking
    c) contraindicated
    d) feather stroking

13. Effleurage over small areas such as the face is usually performed with the _____
    a) fingers
    b) palm of hand
    c) heel of hand
    d) elbow

14. Lubricants are spread over an area using _____
    a) feather stroking
    b) superficial gliding strokes
    c) percussion
    d) spatulas

15. Which of the following is not a factor in determining the depth of a deep, gliding movement? _____
    a) pressure exerted
    b) part of hand used
    c) weight of client
    d) intention of application

16. Kneading helps to reduce _____
    a) blood pressure
    b) adhesions
    c) stretch marks
    d) arm strain

17. Moving a superficial layer of tissue against a deeper layer of tissue is called _____
    a) cupping
    b) kneading
    c) friction
    d) deep pressure

18. A technique that causes an increase in the amount of blood in an area of hyperemia is _____
    a) percussion
    b) skin rolling
    c) deep gliding
    d) compression

19. Heat makes the connective tissues around muscles _____
    a) stronger
    b) more pliable
    c) stiffer
    d) longer

20. Chucking, rolling, wringing, and shaking are types of friction applied when massaging the _____
    a) back
    b) arms and legs
    c) stiffer
    d) face

21. Shaking and rocking are used extensively in this method: _____
    a) Trager®
    b) Chinese
    c) Swedish
    d) German

22. Nerve trunks and centers are sometimes chosen as sites for the application of _____
    a) rolling
    b) rocking
    c) pressure
    d) vibration

23. The preferred technique to reduce fibrosis and the formation of scar tissue at the site of a soft tissue injury is _____
    a) deep touch
    c) active joint movements
    b) deep gliding
    d) transverse friction massage

24. A mechanical vibrator that has a back-and-forth movement is called   _____
    a) orbital   c) vertical
    b) oscillating   d) horizontal

25. A mechanical vibrator that has a circular movement is called   _____
    a) oscillating   c) orbital
    b) round   d) global

26. Movements that include tapping, beating, or slapping are called   _____
    a) percussion   c) vibration
    b) touching   d) fulling

27. When doing passive joint movements, the change in the quality of movement as the limb reaches the extent of its possible range is termed   _____
    a) range of movement   c) end feel
    b) stretch   d) pathological barrier

28. Active joint movements require that the client   _____
    a) contract muscles   c) lift weights
    b) keep relaxed   d) dance

Chapter 11
Application of Massage Technique

1. The proper application of massage technique uses the practitioner's _____
   a) palms
   b) entire body
   c) shoulders
   d) fingers

2. The most important tools used by a massage practitioner are the _____
   a) hands
   b) vibrators
   c) massage tables
   d) lotions

3. The first rule in massage and bodywork is _____
   a) greet the client in a friendly manner
   b) always refer to other health practitioners when indicated
   c) determine indications and contraindications before starting the massage
   d) do no harm

4. The observation of body postures in relation to safe and efficient movement in daily living activities is called _____
   a) physical boundaries
   b) body language
   c) assessment techniques
   d) body mechanics

5. To increase power and conserve energy when giving massages, the practitioner should _____
   a) lift weights
   b) exercise daily
   c) use their entire body
   d) breathe deeply and concentrate

6. Preventing backaches and conserving strength is achieved through _____
   a) exercise
   b) correct posture
   c) weight lifting
   d) diet

7. The degree of misalignment of the supporting structures of the body is termed _____
   a) body mechanics
   b) joint angle
   c) range of motion
   d) biomechanical deviation

8. The concept that you have a geographical center in your body is called _____
   a) centering
   b) chi
   c) channeling
   d) grounding

9. The concept that you have a connection with the client and help him or her to release unwanted tension and stress is called _____
   a) channeling
   b) centering
   c) grounding
   d) counseling

10. The pattern or design of a massage is called _____
    a) touch
    b) stroke
    c) sequence
    d) plan

Chapter 12
Procedures for Complete Body Massage

1. The most effective way to receive a massage is
   a) fully clothed
   b) partially clothed
   c) with all clothing removed
   d) wearing loose-fitting clothing
   _____

2. A client's modesty is protected with proper
   a) draping
   b) communication
   c) grooming
   d) clothing
   _____

3. The draping method that covers the table and wraps the client with a single linen is called
   a) top cover
   b) full sheet
   c) diaper
   d) wrapping
   _____

4. Oil is applied with this stroke:
   a) petrissage
   b) tapotement
   c) effleurage
   d) friction
   _____

5. A client with osteoporosis should not have a neck massage that includes:
   a) petrissage
   b) friction
   c) joint massage
   d) effleurage
   _____

6. Percussion should not be applied to the back area over the
   a) spine
   b) kidneys
   c) lungs
   d) heart
   _____

7. When the massage is finished and it time for the client to get up and off the table, the practitioner should
   a) leave the room and give the client privacy
   b) turn their backs to prevent the client's embarrassment
   c) instruct them to be careful getting up
   d) assist them into a sitting position and support the table, maintaining contact with them as they stand up
   _____

8. The therapeutic procedure involves all of the following EXCEPT
   a) assessment
   b) planning
   c) performance
   d) psychological evaluation
   _____

9. The purpose of performing a client assessment is
   a) to diagnose the cause of the clientsproblem
   b) to reduce the chance of being suedfor improper practice
   c) to establish a base line of the client's functional ability in order to track their improvement.
   d) all of the above
   _____

10. Muscle tissues, tendons, and muscle attachments are called
    a) contractile tissues
    b) inert tissues
    c) end feel
    d) capsular patterns
    _____

11. Bones and ligaments are examples of
    a) contractile tissues
    b) inert tissues
    c) end feel
    d) capsular patterns

12. When assessing range of motion, first test the client's
    a) painful joints
    b) pain tolerance
    c) strength
    d) good side

13. Pain and how the client reacts to it is called a/an
    a) subjective finding
    b) objective finding
    c) active movement
    d) contraindication

14. Limitation of a joint movement due to the stretching of fibrous tissues is called
    a) hard end feel
    b) springy end feel
    c) soft end feel
    d) acute inflammation

15. The source of pain can be pinpointed through
    a) palpation
    b) hard end feel
    c) inert tissues
    d) range of motion

16. Determining if goals have been met is called
    a) goal tending
    b) processing
    c) evaluation
    d) assessment

1. All of the following are benefits of face massage EXCEPT
   a) improved circulation
   b) firmer muscles
   c) blackhead removal
   d) toned skin
   _____

2. Whether or not to include face and scalp massage for a client should be determined during the
   a) consultation
   b) referral
   c) rest period
   d) back massage
   _____

3. A contraindication for face massage is:
   a) wrinkles
   b) allergies
   c) contact lenses
   d) dry skin
   _____

4. An accepted method of facial cleansing is with
   a) tissue
   b) facial sponges
   c) cotton swabs
   d) paper towels
   _____

5. Lip color should be removed by using cleansing lotion on a
   a) tissue
   b) washcloth
   c) paper towel
   d) cotton ball
   _____

6. Facial effleurage is performed using the
   a) palm
   b) vibrator
   c) fingertips
   d) steamer
   _____

7. Grasping the skin and flesh gently between the thumb and forefinger in a kneading movement is called
   a) friction
   b) palming
   c) feathering
   d) petrissage
   _____

8. The most stimulating form of massage is
   a) vibration
   b) tapotement
   c) friction
   d) feathering
   _____

9. In scalp massage, firm strokes are
   a) downward
   b) sideways
   c) upward
   d) diagonal
   _____

Chapter 14
Hydrotherapy

1. A popular electrical apparatus used in massage is the _____
   a) heating pad   c) adjustable table
   b) vibrator   d) heat lamp

2. A short application of cold is _____
   a) anesthetizing   c) contraindicated
   b) chilling   d) stimulating

3. Thermal treatments below 32°F or above 115°F may cause _____
   a) tissue damage   c) reduced lymph flow
   b) overstimulation   d) burns

4. Prolonged application of cold leads to a physical condition called _____
   a) freezing   c) hypothermia
   b) hyperthermia   d) freezer burn

5. Heating pads and infrared radiation are types of _____
   a) moist heat   c) diathermy
   b) dry heat   d) solar gain

6. Hydrotherapy is the therapeutic use of _____
   a) heat   c) cold
   b) water   d) massage

7. Saunas and steam baths should be avoided by people with heart conditions or _____
   a) diabetes   c) arthritis
   b) swollen glands   d) muscle spasms

8. A local application of cold will _____
   a) cause reddening due to vasoconstriction   c) increase the pulse rate
   b) increase leukocyte migration to the area   d) have an analgesic effect

9. Cold applied for therapeutic purposes is called _____
   a) cryptology   c) RICE
   b) cryotherapy   d) hypotherapy

10. Ice is used on some injuries to prevent _____
    a) swelling   c) pain
    b) bruising   d) all of the above

11. To increase circulation to an injured area and promote healing, alternate applications of _____
    a) vibration and friction   c) heat and cold
    b) feathering and kneading   d) percussion and gliding

12. An economical alternative to commercial ice packs is a plastic bag containing a 2:1 mixture of crushed ice and _____
    a) vinegar   c) bleach
    b) isopropyl alcohol   d) antifreeze

13. Water is a valuable therapeutic agent for all of the following reasons EXCEPT _____
    a) it is inexpensive to use   c) it requires special equipment
    b) it is readily available   d) it absorbs and conducts heat

14. Water temperatures that are above or below body temperature have this effect: _____
    a) mechanical   c) chemical
    b) thermal   d) psychological

15. Sprays, whirlpools, and friction are examples of this effect: _____
    a) mechanical   c) chemical
    b) thermal   d) psycho-somatic

16. Drinking water is an example of this effect: _____
    a) mechanical   c) chemical
    b) thermal   d) dietary

17. Cardiac conditions, diabetes, lung disease, and high or low blood pressure are examples of hydrotherapy _____
    a) contraindications   c) indications
    b) complications   d) benefits

18. The average temperature of the skin's surface is _____
    a) 98.6°F   c) 89.6°F
    b) 92°   d) 94°F

19. Prolonged use of cold applications has this effect _____
    a) stimulating   c) depressing
    b) energizing   d) dizzying

20. Expansion of blood vessels following cold application is called a/an _____
    a) primary effect   c) afterthought
    b) secondary effect   d) contraindication

21. A bath with water 67∞F to 75∞F is considered _____
    a) cool   c) tepid
    b) cold   d) warm.

22. A bath with a water temperature of 85°F to 95·F is considered _____
    a) cool   c) tepid
    b) cold   d) hot

23. A cold bath shocks the body's _____
    a) heart   c) thyroid
    b) nervous system   d) kidneys

24. A Swedish shampoo is also called a _____
    a) tub massage   c) body shampoo
    b) salt bath   d) herb wrap

25. The frictional application of wet salt over the body is called a _____
    a) salt rub   c) brine massage
    b) saline soak   d) Swedish shampoo

1. The massage movements most frequently used by nurses are   _____
   a) Chinese   c) German
   b) Greek   d) Swedish

2. Increased oxygen supply to cells, elimination of metabolic wastes, and
   decreased blood pressure are some massage   _____
   a) contraindications   c) indications
   b) restrictions   d) benefits

3. Massage benefits the nervous system by   _____
   a) improving skin tone   c) relieving pain
   b) eliminating waste material d) stimulating muscles

4. Massage benefits the skin by   _____
   a) relieving stiffness   c) opening pores
   b) improving tone   d) removing wrinkles

5. To reduce adhesions and fibrosis, this movement is used: _____
   a) crossfiber friction   c) percussion
   b) wringing   d) gliding

6. Massage is not performed on an area that is   _____
   a) bleeding   c) burned
   b) swollen   d) all the above

7. A sore that has not healed properly, persistent hoarseness, or persistent
   coughing are all warning signs of   _____
   a) tuberculosis   c) influenza
   b) cancer   d) emphysema

8. Moving a joint without assistance or resistance is called   _____
   a) flexion   c) extension
   b) range of motion   d) free movement

9. By placing one hand above the joint to be moved and the other below, the
   nurse can control joint   _____
   a) movement   c) strength
   b) rotation   d) discomfort

10. An alcohol rubdown is often   _____
    a) drying   c) vigorous
    b) moisturizing   d) refreshing

11. To lower body temperature, nurses often use a/an   _____
    a) wet blanket   c) oil rubdown
    b) alcohol rubdown   d) Greek massage

12. The alcohol used in rubdowns is   _____
    a) pure grain   c) isopropyl
    b) fermented   d) distilled

1. Kinesiology is the study of
   a) muscles
   b) cells
   c) body movement
   d) muscle strength
   _____

2. Blood remaining in muscle for an extended period is called
   a) hyperemia
   b) hypertension
   c) hyperthermia
   d) ischemia
   _____

3. Compression strokes in athletic massage use the
   a) knuckles
   b) forearm
   c) fingertips
   d) palm
   _____

4. A trigger point causes pain to
   a) radiate
   b) evaporate
   c) dissipate
   d) increase
   _____

5. Shaking and jostling are performed on muscles that are
   a) large
   b) small
   c) injured
   d) relaxed
   _____

6. The therapist-assisted active and resistive patterned movements used in the rehabilitation of disabilities are commonly known as
   a) MET
   b) PNF
   c) ROM
   d) PHD
   _____

7. MET helps to counteract
   a) soft tissue injury
   b) headache
   c) sprains
   d) muscle spasm
   _____

8. Pre-event massage should be given this far in advance of an event:
   a) 30 minutes
   b) 2 days
   c) 2 hours
   d) 6 hours
   _____

9. The most beneficial form of massage for athletes is
   a) pre-event
   b) post-event
   c) training
   d) rehabilitative
   _____

10. A sprain with mild pain and minimal loss of function is classified as
    a) Grade I
    b) Grade II
    c) Grade III
    d) Grade IV
    _____

11. A sprain with some tearing of fibrous tissue is classified as
    a) Grade I
    b) Grade II
    c) Grade III
    d) Grade IV
    _____

12. Injuries that have a gradual onset or recur often are called

    a) sprains   c) acute

    b) occupational   d) chronic

13. An injury in or between muscle fibers is called

    a) macrotrauma   c) chronic

    b) microtrauma   d) acute

1. Small, thin-walled tubes that collect lymph from interstitial fluid are called _____
   a) lymph capillaries
   b) lymph nodes
   c) plasma ducts
   d) lacteals

2. Lymph vessels in the walls of the small intestine that carry away fat are called _____
   a) fat blockers
   b) lacteals
   c) adipose ducts
   d) lymph capillaries

3. Submaxillary lymph nodes are located under the _____
   a) cranium
   b) tongue
   c) armpit
   d) stomach

4. A bodywork technique that attempts to bring the structure of the body into alignment around a central axis is called _____
   a) structural integration
   b) Trager®
   c) MET
   d) NMT

5. Realignment of muscular and connective tissue and reshaping the body's physical posture is called _____
   a) chiropractic
   b) centering
   c) Rolfing®
   d) Trager®

6. A hyper-irritable spot that is painful when compressed is called a/an _____
   a) trigger point
   b) pain point
   c) acupressure point
   d) alarm point

7. Digital pressure directly into the trigger point is called _____
   a) ischemic compression
   b) probing
   c) stretch and spray
   d) palpating

8. Using neurophysical muscle reflexes to improve the functional mobility of the joints is called _____
   a) kneading
   b) NMT
   c) muscle energy technique
   d) stretching

9. The technique based on the theory that as soon as a strong muscle contraction releases, the muscle relaxes is called _____
   a) contract relax
   b) antagonist contraction
   c) contract the opposite
   d) fibrosis reduction

10. Positioning and supporting patients in pain-free, comfortable positions is called _____
    a) transition
    b) muscle energy technique
    c) strain-counter/strain
    d) massaging

11. The correct application of the natural laws of life is called _____
    a) Swedish massage   c) medicine
    b) legality   d) orthobionomy

12. Precision muscle testing, passive positioning, directional massage, and deep pressure are the physical techniques used in _____
    a) SMB   c) ROM
    b) NMT   d) PNF

13. A type of specialized kinesiology used to evaluate energetic imbalances in the body is called: _____
    a) SMB   c) Orthobionomy
    b) precision muscle testing d) tender point therapy

14. The procedure that gently moves contracted tissues into the direction of contraction while bringing the ends of the hypercontracted muscle tissue closer together is called _____
    a) neuromuscular therapy   c) positional release
    b) tender point   d) reflex

15. Acupuncture, shiatsu, polarity, and reflexology are examples of _____
    a) energetic manipulation   c) reactive circuits
    b) behavioral therapy   d) age recession

16. The philosophical Chinese term for the energy existing in life is _____
    a) *chi*   c) *yang*
    b) *yin*   d) Tao

17. Energy circulates the body in a network called _____
    a) force field   c) vesicles
    b) meridians   d) organs

18. Meridians have been mapped on the body according to location and direction of _____
    a) muscle movement   c) energy flow
    b) connective tissue   d) blood vessels

19. The approximate number of acupoints located on the 12 major meridians is _____
    a) 395   c) 50
    b) 1000   d) 175

20. The Japanese finger pressure method to increase circulation and relieve stress is called _____
    a) acupressure   c) amma
    b) tsubo   d) shiatsu

21. Reflexologists believe that headache can be cured by performing reflex massage on the _____
    a) big toe   c) thumb
    b) wrist   d) ankle

Chapter 18
Therapeutic Exercise

1. The body's ability to tolerate increased load is called _____
   a) exercise   c) adaptation
   b) stress management   d) muscle building

2. The ability of a muscle or muscle group to contract and produce tension
   with a resultant maximum force exerted on some resistance is called _____
   a) strength   c) adaptation
   b) pressure   d) endurance

3. Strength is in direct proportion to a muscle's _____
   a) length   c) size
   b) location   d) type

4. All of the muscle fibers controlled by a single motor neuron are called a _____
   a) motor unit   c) neuromuscular connection
   b) muscle bundle   d) motor end point

5. To increase strength, muscles must be _____
   a) lengthened   c) shortened
   b) overloaded   d) massaged

6. Maximum resistance with low reps tends to build _____
   a) endurance   c) strength and bulk
   b) cramps   d) fluid

7. Lighter resistance with more repetitions builds _____
   a) endurance   c) strength
   b) cramps   d) size

8. Early gains in a strengthening program are often the result of better _____
   a) weights   c) diet
   b) machines   d) nerve recruitment

9. When the force of the contraction is equal to the resistance and the muscle
   length remains the same, the contraction is called _____
   a) isotonic   c) concentric
   b) isometric   d) eccentric

10. When a contracted muscle shortens during the contraction, it is called _____
    a) isokinetic   c) concentric
    b) isometric   d) eccentric

11. When a contracted muscle lengthens, the contraction is called _____
    a) isokinetic   c) concentric
    b) isometric   d) eccentric

12. Isokinetic exercise is done
    a) on machines
    b) with free weights
    c) at home
    d) during dance aerobics

13. In manual resistance exercises, the resistance is provided by
    a) machines
    b) the therapist
    c) free weights
    d) the patient

14. An example of a body weight exercise is
    a) jogging
    b) situps
    c) jump rope
    d) weight lifting

15. The ability to carry on an activity over a prolonged period of time and resist fatigue is called
    a) strength
    b) aerobics
    c) endurance
    d) exercise

16. The amount of overload put on the body during exercise is called
    a) frequency
    b) weight
    c) intensity
    d) stress

17. Duration is an exercise session's
    a) length
    b) frequency
    c) output
    d) intensity

18. The ability of a joint to move freely and painlessly through its range of motion is called
    a) extension
    b) contraction
    c) exercise
    d) flexibility

19. The ability of tissues to adapt to ongoing stresses and conditions is called
    a) plasticity
    b) elasticity
    c) flexibility
    d) adaptability

20. High-velocity, high-intensity stretching movements of low duration are called
    a) aerobic
    b) flexing
    c) ballistic
    d) stretching

21. Better flexibility is the result of
    a) sustained stretching
    b) ballistic stretching
    c) weight lifting
    d) aerobic exercise

22. The neuromuscular process of using the correct sequence of muscular movements with the right timing and force is called
    a) relaxation
    b) breathing
    c) massage
    d) coordination

1. A positive self-image means that you
   a) like yourself and what you do
   b) look beautiful
   c) wear expensive clothes
   d) are vain
   _____

2. Your public image includes all of the following EXCEPT
   a) appearance
   b) business conduct
   c) expense reports
   d) customer relations
   _____

3. Clarifying your business's purpose, stating a mission, setting goals, and determining priorities is called
   a) accounting
   b) business planning
   c) tax preparation
   d) job training
   _____

4. A short, general statement of the business's main focus is called a/an
   a) goal
   b) business plan
   c) advertisement
   d) mission statement
   _____

5. A business that has one owner is called a
   a) sole proprietorship
   b) partnership
   c) corporation
   d) limited liability company
   _____

6. A business that has stockholders is called a
   a) sole proprietorship
   b) partnership
   c) corporation
   d) subsidiary
   _____

7. Undercapitalization and poor management are the two main reasons for small business
   a) expansion
   b) insurance
   c) failure
   d) advertising
   _____

8. When buying an established business, make sure it is
   a) well established
   b) reputable
   c) in a good location
   d) all of the above
   _____

9. The insurance that covers costs of injuries occurring on your property and any resulting litigation is called _____ insurance.
   a) disability
   b) liability
   c) homeowners
   d) workman's compensation
   _____

10. Insurance that protects the therapist from lawsuits filed by a client, due to injury or loss from negligence or poor execution of a professional skill, is called
    a) liability
    b) disability
    c) compensation
    d) malpractice
    _____

11. Insurance that covers the medical costs for employees injured on the job is called _____
    a) worker's compensation
    b) malpractice
    c) liability
    d) disability

12. A ledger that separates and classifies every business expenditure is called a/an _____
    a) inventory
    b) disbursement record
    c) profit/loss statement
    d) balance sheet

13. All of the following are business expenses EXCEPT _____
    a) rent
    b) supplies
    c) advertising
    d) owner's salary

14. The marketing activity done in return for direct payment is called _____
    a) publicity
    b) advertising
    c) bartering
    d) referral

15. Developing personal and professional contacts for the purpose of giving and receiving support and sharing information is called _____
    a) hobnobbing
    b) networking
    c) advertising
    d) promotions

16. The best and least expensive way to create new business is through _____
    a) referrals
    b) advertising
    c) public speaking
    d) client retention

17. Social Security and unemployment compensation are two regulations of the _____
    a) state government
    b) federal government
    c) county government
    d) city government

18. Sales taxes, licenses, and worker's compensation are required by _____
    a) state government
    b) federal government
    c) county government
    d) city government

19. A person hired on as his or her own boss is called a/an _____
    a) employee
    b) bookkeeper
    c) independent contractor
    d) receptionist

ANSWERS

Historical Overview of Massage

1-b	5-d	9-d	13-d	17-a
2-d	6-a	10-d	14-d	18-b
3-b	7-a	11-a	15-c	19-a
4-c	8-a	12-c	16-d	20-b

Requirements for the Practice of Therapeutic Massage

1-a	3-c	5-a	7-c	9-d
2-b	4-a	6-d	8-a	

Professional Ethics for Massage Practitioners

1-d	2-b	3-a	4-a	5-d

Human Anatomy and Physiology Overview

1-b	7-b	13-c	19-d	25-d
2-a	8-c	14-a	20-b	26-e
3-c	9-a	15-c	21-b	27-d
4-a	10-c	16-b	22-c	28-b
5-b	11-b	17-d	23-b	29-c
6-d	12-b	18-c	24-a	

Human Anatomy and Physiology

1-c	24-b	47-c	70-a	93-a
2-c	25-b	48-b	71-a	94-a
3-b	26-a	49-c	72-a	95-c
4-b	27-c	50-a	73-b	96-b
5-b	28-a	51-b	74-a	97-a
6-d	29-a	52-b	75-d	98-d
7-d	30-c	53-c	76-b	99-a
8-a	31-a	54-a	77-b	100-a
9-b	32-c	55-d	78-c	101-c
10-a	33-b	56-d	79-b	102-c
11-b	34-b	57-c	80-a	103-c
12-a	35-b	58-a	81-c	104-a
13-a	36-d	59-b	82-a	105-d
14-b	37-d	60-a	83-b	106-b
15-a	38-c	61-c	84-a	107-d
16-c	39-c	62-c	85-c	
17-a	40-c	63-b	86-d	
18-c	41-a	64-a	87-a	
19-a	42-c	65-b	88-c	
20-d	43-b	66-c	89-b	
21-c	44-a	67-a	90-d	
22-b	45-c	68-b	91-c	
23-c	46-c	69-c	92-b	

Effects, Benefits, Indications, and Contraindications of Massage

1-a	6-d	11-a	16-b
2-c	7-b	12-c	17-d
3-a	8-b	13-b	18-b
4-b	9-d	14-a	
5-b	10-c	15-c	

Equipment and Products

1-b	3-c	5-c	7-b
2-a	4-c	6-b	8-a

Sanitary and Safety Practices

1-b	5-a	9-b	13-b
2-b	6-d	10-a	
3-d	7-c	11-c	
4-b	8-a	12-d	

The Consultation

1-b	4-b	7-a	10-c
2-d	5-a	8-d	
3-d	6-c	9-b	

Classification of Massage Movements

1-a	8-a	15-c	22-c
2-c	9-c	16-b	23-d
3-d	10-a	17-c	24-b
4-b	11-c	18-d	25-c
5-a	12-b	19-b	26-a
6-d	13-a	20-b	27-c
7-c	14-b	21-a	28-a

Application of Massage Technique

1-b	4-d	7-d	10-c
2-a	5-c	8-a	
3-d	6-b	9-c	

Procedures for Complete Body Massage

1-c	5-c	9-c	13-a
2-a	6-b	10-a	14-b
3-b	7-d	11-b	15-a
4-c	8-d	12-d	16-c

Face and Scalp Massage

1-c	4-b	7-d
2-a	5-a	8-b
3-b	6-c	9-c

Hydrotherapy

1-b	8-d	15-a	22-c
2-d	9-b	16-c	23-b
3-a	10-d	17-a	24-c
4-c	11-c	18-b	25-a
5-b	12-b	19-c	
6-b	13-c	20-b	
7-a	14-b	21-a	

Massage for Nursing and Healthcare

1-d	4-b	7-b	10-d
2-d	5-a	8-d	11-b
3-c	6-d	9-b	12-c

Athletic/Sports Massage

1-c	5-d	9-c	13-b
2-a	6-b	10-a	
3-d	7-d	11-b	
4-a	8-a	12-d	

Specialized Techniques

1-a	7-a	13-b	19-a
2-b	8-c	14-c	20-d
3-b	9-a	15-a	21-a
4-a	10-c	16-a	
5-c	11-d	17-b	
6-a	12-a	18-c	

Therapeutic Exercise

1-c	7-a	13-b	19-a
2-a	8-d	14-b	20-c
3-c	9-b	15-c	21-a
4-a	10-c	16-c	22-d
5-b	11-d	17-a	
6-c	12-a	18-d	

Business Practices

1-a	6-c	11-a	16-a
2-c	7-c	12-b	17-b
3-b	8-d	13-d	18-a
4-d	9-b	14-b	19-c
5-a	10-d	15-b	